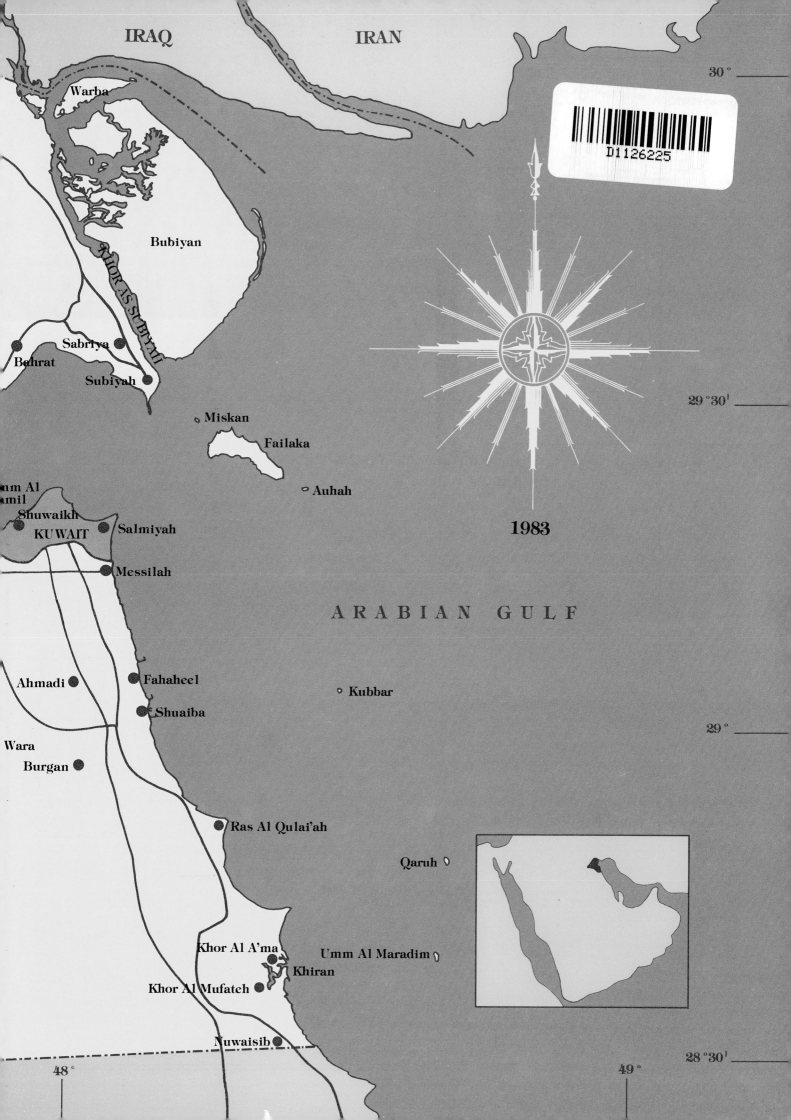

Kuwait's
Natural History

An Introduction

Editor   David Clayton
Associate Editor   Charles Pilcher

Abdul Razzak Mulla Hussain
Deputy Chairman, Kuwait Petroleum Corporation

Kuwait Petroleum Corporation has the honour of presenting this book to you, being the culmination of continuous scientific research and study in the field of natural history of the State of Kuwait.

This book is indeed a pioneering endeavour which tackles its subject on an accurate and indisputable scientific basis. It is the first publication to deal with a purely scientific subject brimming over with valuable data on animal, plant and bird species in the Kuwaiti environment.

We must, in this instance, acknowledge with gratitude the fruitful efforts and constructive ideas of all those who took part in bringing forth this precious scientific study and, in presenting it in its attractive form for the reader to enjoy. We are especially indebted to members of the Ahmadi Natural History and Field Studies Group some of whom are professors and researchers at Kuwait University, who must take primary credit for compiling, classifying and arranging the contents of this valuable book. We also commend the efforts of Kuwait Oil Company which supervised this scientific book.

We are confident that the reader will benefit from the scientific data contained herein and hope that it will be the start of intensive efforts towards highlighting a true picture of the Kuwaiti environment for the benefit of our present and future generations. We also hope that our descendants will continue study and research in this field, to enrich and add to the knowledge of mankind.

Kuwait Petroleum Corporation, with H.E. The Minister of Oil, Sheikh Ali Al-Khalifa Al-Sabah as Chairman, will spare no effort to provide assistance and support to any endeavour that would honour the name of Kuwait.

Dame Violet Dickson O.B.E

Arrived in Kuwait 1929

In my early days here I remember how the arrival of the autumn rains, heralding the appearance of the colourful flowering annuals, was greeted with pleasure. Later in early spring, the rain brought the Bedouin their truffles or 'fuga' which were a most nourishing and enjoyable part of their simple diet.

The hot summers were spent in settled well areas but during autumn and spring the flocks of sheep and camels were continuously moving from one grazing area to another. This annual migration prevented overgrazing and was therefore a form of conservation. Not only were the 'Arfaj' and 'Hamdh' bushes protected but they in turn sheltered the less hardy plants from the icy winter winds and blown sand.

Today it can be easy to forget the importance of the desert and the sea to Kuwait's natural heritage. The intelligent study of the animal and plant communities will help us to understand the vital importance to us of their place in the world which we share with them. I am sure that you will find this a most interesting book including as it does, so many photographs of the plants and animals of Kuwait. I hope it will help young people especially to learn about their surroundings. It should also serve as a timely reminder to all that the desert and marine communities are hardy, yet fragile ones, easily disturbed. Perhaps with care and a knowledge of the rich natural history of the desert we can return it to its former glory where Hubara and Gazelle are once more found.

Ahmadi Natural History Group

c/o Kuwait Oil Company. (KSC)

The Ahmadi Natural History and Field Studies Group was formed in 1969 under the sponsorship of Kuwait Oil Company and the patronage of the Group's current President, Mr. Faisal Thunayyan Al-Ghanim. The basic aims of the Group are threefold. Firstly the Group acts as a forum for those interested in natural history in general and as a focal point for the study of Kuwait's plants and animals in particular. Secondly the Group encourages field studies and thirdly it maintains contact with other institutions to help disseminate knowledge of the local scene.

In addition to the usual officers the Group has Recorders for each main area of interest. They are responsible for documenting records and findings, co-ordinating activities in their specific fields and giving advice and assistance to members. As far as is possible regular twice monthly illustrated talks on a wide variety of topics are given by invited speakers and during the cooler months field trips are arranged. In a work-room at Kuwait Oil Company's Hubara Centre there is a small reference library for the use of members. News-letters are produced periodically to provide information about the Group's activities as well as special articles dealing with aspects of natural history in Kuwait. These have included lists of the birds and plants and even a guide to gardening in Kuwait.

The strength and success of the Ahmadi Natural History and Field Studies Group depend on its members and the Group is always pleased to welcome new members.

Failaka seal. The 4000 year old steatite stamp seal is a particularly appropriate emblem for the A.N.H.G. It depicts a gazelle and a bird standing on what might be a net or a fish trap (By courtesy of the Director of Kuwait Museum).

Our First Natural History Book

Editor   David Clayton
Associate Editor   Charles Pilcher
Technical Editor   Sarah Jones

This book would not have been possible without the support of many people and it is appropriate to thank them all unreservedly.

In particular, we are indebted to Kuwait Oil Company for encouraging us in the preparation of the material for this book and for undertaking the task of having this book published. On behalf of the Group's President, Mr. Faisal Thunayyan Al-Ghanim, the Officers and members of the Group and the many contributors to this book we wish to thank, specially, Mr. Ahmad Mohd. Ja'afar, Mr. Sulaiman A. Al-Mutawwa, Mr. Mohammad Jasim Abdul Salam, Mr. Saud Faraj Al Hajrie, Mr. Hamed Yousef Al-Gharabally, Mr. Haider J.M. Ahmad and Mr. Ali H. Murad of Kuwait Oil Company (KSC).

The responsibility for the contents of this book, however, for the selection and accuracy of the material presented and for the layout and style, lies, needless to say, with the Editors.

Members of the Ahmadi Natural History Group Committee who have been involved include Mrs. K. MacIntyre, who provided the original scheme for a volume on the flora and fauna of Kuwait, and Mrs. J. Kendall, Miss V.R. Koymans, Mr. G. Bealey, Mrs. O. Blackburn and Mr. M. Deeks who implemented its execution.

Identification of specimens and photographs was undertaken by Mr. R. Aldridge, Dr. E.N. Arnold, Mr. S. Bacchns, Dr. P.C. Barnard, Mr. B. Bolton, Mrs. S. Brooks, Professor J.L. Cloudsley-Thompson, Mr. M.C. Day, Professor E.S. Demian, Mr. E.J. Goodridge, Dr. D.L. Harrison, Ms. D.M. Hills, Mr. P.O. Hillyard, Mr. F.R. Hinkle, Mr. H.L. MacIntyre, Ms. J. Marshall, Mr. F.C. Naggs, Mr. A.T. Pittaway, Mr. A.C. Pont, Dr. K. Relyea, Mrs. K.R. Smythe, Professor M. Vachon, Mr. C.R. Vardy, Dr. T.C. Vaughan, Mr. F.R. Wanless and Mr. A.C. Wheeler. Any remaining errors are the sole responsibility of the Editors.

Suggestions and comments on earlier drafts were offered by Professor J.L. Cloudsley-Thompson, Mrs. V. Armer, Dr. D.A. Jones, Professor E.S. Demian and Mr. L. Barnes. The men at the Pearl Oyster market and Mr. Salam Al-Ablani assisted in the preparation of the Traditional Fishing Chapter.

Mr. K. Mahmood Akbar, Mrs. J. Kendall, Mrs. S. Lacy, Mrs. S. Ljnbic, Mrs. C. Gonsalvez, Mrs. S. Avarachan and Mrs. I. Deeks were involved in typing of the several drafts. Mr. S. Morgan drew the map.

The plates were selected from several thousand 35 mm slides and thanks are due to all who submitted slides. The photographers are identified by their initials which are parenthesized at the end of each plate legend. The photographers were:

Mr. Nick Atkins, (NRA); Mr. John Bradley, (JB); Mr. Bish Brown, (JNBB); Mr. Arthur Caldwell, (AC); Dr. David Clayton, (DAC); Mr. Leon Corral, (LC); Dr. Richard Criddle, (RSC); Mr. Michael Deeks, (MD); Dr. Nigel Downing, (ND); Fahad Al Marzouk, (FAM); Dr. Tony Farmer, (ASDF); Mr. Eddie Goodridge, (EJG); Dr. Riad Halwagy, (RH); Mr. Paul Haynes, (PRH); Dr. Charles Johnson, (CTJ); Dr. David Jones, (DAJ); Kuwait Oil Company, (KOC); Ms. Vicki Koymans, (VRK); Mrs. Kate MacIntyre, (KJM); Dr. Ian McFarlaine, (IDM); Ministry of Information, (MIK); Dr. Charles Pilcher, (CWTP); Dr. Don Poultney, (DPP); Mrs. G. Relyea, (GR); Dr. Kenneth Relyea, (KR); Mr. Tony Saunders, (AJS); Mr. Mahmoud Shihab, (MS); Mr. Bill Stuart, (WAS); Dr. Thomas Vaughan, (TCV); Mr. Ian Walker, (IW); Mr. George Warren, (GWW); Mr. Rainer Wendt, (RW); Unknown contributors, (ANHG); Dr. Nicholas van Zalinqe, (NPvZ).

An Arabic translation of this volume has been prepared by Professor E.S. Demian who died before the book's publication. His translation is his testimonial.

In recent years there has been a tremendous increase in publications cataloguing the fauna and flora of the Arabian Gulf and Peninsula. Most of this information is contained in either the scientific literature which is not readily available to the layman, or in the form of specialised books dealing with a single group of animals or plants. This book attempts to present a general picture of, and an appreciation for, the environments and biological communities that occur in Kuwait. If the book achieves this aim and further encourages readers to seek more knowledge of their environment then it will have more than succeeded.

The text of this book was completed in March 1981 and in some respects is already out-of-date. At the time of writing, there was no floral national emblem. Early 1983, however, *Rhanterium epapposum*, better known as 'Arfaj', was adopted as Kuwait's national plant. The yellow scorpions mentioned in the chapter on land invertebrates were unidentified but now it is possible to say that there are two common species *Compsobuthus arabicus* and *Buthacus leptochelys*. A third, *Apistobuthus pterygocercus*, is a relatively rare species and its discovery in Kuwait represents a range extension for the species. The freshwater pool at Jahra mentioned in the chapter on conservation has been refilled, re-establishing its importance as an overwintering area for many migratory birds.

Probably the most significant development, however, has been the establishment of The Regional Organisation for the Protection of the Marine Environment (ROPME). With its headquarters and executive council based in Kuwait, this organisation is beginning a new era in local conservation.

Sponsors

KUWAIT PETROLEUM CORPORATION

KUWAIT OIL COMPANY

Published by: Kuwait Oil Company, Kuwait.

Designed & Printed by Fahad Al Marzouk, Kuwait.

Contents

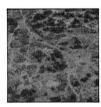

Country &
Climate

By
David Clayton

To some people Kuwait is simply a small barren area of desert bordering the north-western corner of the Arabian Gulf. It would indeed be untrue to claim that Kuwait is a place of spectacular scenery and magnificent wildlife but the country does have a beauty of its own. The secret lies in the contrast, the scale, the simplicity, the unexpectedness and in the adaptations shown by the plants and animals to their environment. The following pages can provide only a glimpse of this natural beauty but should convince even the hardened sceptic that Kuwait has much to offer, be it the sight of the yellow and purple carpet of flowers that transforms the desert after rains, a line of migrating Steppe Eagles gliding over the Jal Az-Zor Ridge or simply the form and texture of wind-sculptured sand.

Wadi Al-Baten. During spring the desert can be transformed by the sudden appearance of carpets of flowers. The ungrazed gully sides of the Wadi yield many different plants, the predominant one here being the annual *Diplotaxis acris*. (KJM)

Even in a publication of this length there are many reasons why it is not possible to present a complete record of Kuwait's natural history. In some cases there are simply too many different species to mention: over 400 different plants, 220 birds and 350 fish have been identified and, whilst the reptiles, amphibians and mammals are numbered in tens rather than hundreds, little is specifically known of their life styles. The marine and land invertebrates can also be counted in hundreds but unfortunately our ignorance, as well as the need for brevity, prevents mention of many. Relatively few have been specifically identified and consequently little more than generalizations can be made about them. Nevertheless it is hoped that the reader will find some interesting and even fascinating information in the following pages and that the book will help to encourage an atmosphere which favours the preservation and study of the flora and fauna that are Kuwait's natural heritage.

The photographs are the book's main attraction and the layout and text have been arranged with this in mind. Some chapters, such as those on birds and reptiles, are natural and obvious choices for separate treatment but others, like those dealing with vegetation, terrestrial invertebrates and marine life are more complex and have been treated as single topics for photographic convenience.

The beauty, singularity and sometimes oddity of the animals and plants are clearly shown by the photographs. To a naturalist or biologist these considerations are often incidental and the real beauty of an organism lies in the way in which it has become so well adapted to its environment. This harmony can be expressed in many different ways: in the dependence of the plants for propagation on the very insects that feed on them, in the amazing and mysterious navigational ability of migratory birds and insects, in the ability of some mammals to exist in a desert without drinking water, in the deadly efficiency of the venomous snakes and in the complex food chains of the marine environment.

The balance of nature is established through environmental adaptations of the animals and plants and their close interdependence. It is also a precarious balance, easily upset by thoughtless use of the now awesome power of man to change and modify the environment he inhabits. These then are the themes, interdependence, adaptation and conservation, that are explored and illustrated in the following chapters.

Before moving on to describe the plants and animals it is necessary to mention something of the physical environment. The State of Kuwait is situated at the head of the Arabian Gulf between latitude 28° and 30° north and longitude 46° and 48° east. It is bounded by Iraq to the west and north, by the Arabian Gulf to the east and by Saudi Arabia to the south. The country occupies 17,000 square km of desert and low offshore islands and is a continuation of the Arabian desert, which is itself part of the extensive belt of sub-tropical deserts such as the Sahara, Iranian, Thar (Indian) and Mongolian deserts. These deserts lie beyond the limits of the annual swing of the equatorial rainfall belt at the latitudes in which strong trade winds blow throughout the year.

Jal Az-Zor Escarpment. Composed principally of sedimentary sand- and limestones with some fossiliferous deposits, the Escarpment is one of the main topographical features of the State. (WAS)

The two largest offshore islands, Bubiyan and Warba, are uninhabited and are located adjacent to the Shatt Al-Arab in the north. Failaka, near the entrance to Kuwait Bay, has been inhabited since prehistoric times. Umm Al-Namil in the Bay and Auhah, Kubbar, Qaruh and Umm Al-Maradim to the south are all small, barren and uninhabited.

Jal Az-Zor gully. The soft sedimentary stone is easily scoured by the water draining off the land after heavy rainstorms. The shelter provided by these gullies is one factor responsible for the profusion of animals and plants found here (WAS).

The mainland consists of a flat and slightly undulating plain sloping generally towards the north-east and it is broken by occasional hills, escarpments and depressions. The main topographical feature of the country is the Jal Az-Zor Escarpment, which extends north-eastwards for about 60 km along the north-western shore of Kuwait Bay from Atraf to Bahrat. At its highest the escarpment is 145 m above sea level. From the Bay there is only a gently rising coastal terrace but the Escarpment's height is dramatically emphasised by the steep rock faces beyond the terrace, which are extensively split by gullies that may extend many metres into the rock face. At a height of 137 m, the Ahmadi Ridge is almost as prominent as the Zor Ridge but its gentle east and west slopes disguise its height to all but the most careful observer. It separates the plain of Burgan (the oil field) from the Gulf coast.

The other major feature is the Wadi Al-Baten, which marks the western boundary of the State. In central Kuwait the Wadi is some 6-8 km wide and entrenched 50 m below the level of the plain, a relic of the water-course that once flowed along its length. As the Wadi extends northwards it becomes more shallow. Dense wadi systems occur in northern Kuwait, especially in the Raudhatain and Umm Al-Aish areas where they converge into a fairly large depression. Water drainage is generally internal except along the east coast where the wadis drain into the Khor As-Subiyah. The extent of this sub-surface drainage can be judged from the output of the natural underwater reservoir that was discovered at Raudhatain in 1962. Its daily output of water is some 91 million litres. To the south of the country the desert is largely feature-less except for a few hills in the south-western section of the Partitioned Zone and in the Burgan Field. The most conspicuous hill of the latter group is the Wara Hill. The remaining features of note are Umm Al-Rimam, to the north of the Zor Ridge and the small and shallow depressions or 'playas', which are found in the northern, western and central areas of the country. These are basins that have a fine silt and clay bottom, but with some sand and considerable salt also present. After the winter rains the playas fill with water and form important watering places for the camel herds of the Bedouin.

Finally, there are the sand dunes, without which no sub-tropical desert would be complete. Small coastal dunes are found bordering the Gulf beyond Ras Al-Qulai'ah in the south but true desert sand dunes occur in parts of the Wadi Al-Baten and at Umm Niqa in the north-east. These dunes are mobile, crescent-shaped barchan dunes that, under the influence of the prevailing winds, are steadily advancing towards the Zor Ridge.

The Indo-Pacific Region, of which the Arabian Gulf is part, has the richest marine life on Earth in terms of the number and diversity of species. Compared with the rest of the region, however, the marine life of the Gulf is relatively impoverished. There is an interesting parallel here between the animals and plants of the sea and those of the land. Only those organisms that are able to tol-erate, or have adapted to, the harsh environmental conditions of high and variable temperature and lack of water survive and flourish.

The Gulf is relatively shallow and the sea quickly adapts to the ambient temperature, becoming warm in summer and cold in winter. Being ap-preciably higher than that of the world's oceans, the salinity of the Arabian Gulf effectively makes it more difficult for its inhabitants to obtain the

Umm Al-Rimam. After a dry winter and a hot summer this wadi, which is situated to the north of the Zor Ridge, can be extremely barren. With adequate rainfall however, the variety and profusion of life that appears rivals that of the Wadi Al-Baten and the Zor Ridge (CWTP)

water necessary for life. The Tigris and Euphrates supply the Gulf with its only source of fresh water and do help to reduce the salinity of Kuwait's water to more reasonable levels. However, the dilution effect is partially counteracted by the high rates of water evaporation during the summer. In carrying large quantities of sediment, the fresh water has also been instrumental in establishing considerable intertidal mudflats. This rich environment is utilised by many marine organisms but the water-borne sediment is harmful to others and has prevented their establishment in the area.

If the Arabian Gulf as a whole is not particularly rich in marine life, Kuwait at least is fortunate in having all of the more important marine habitats along her shores. Mudflats surround Kuwait Bay, except along the northern shores of the Dohah peninsula where the tidal flow is strong enough to prevent the sediment from settling. Sandy beaches and rocky outcrops are to be found here and also along the remaining shores of Kuwait to the south. The urban sprawl from Shuwaikh to Messilah has drastically changed the natural coastline but has at the same time provided new habitats to be exploited by the marine life. Rocky outcrops, coral heads and reefs also lie close inshore. Most of these reefs are dead but still provide excellent shelter for many animals, and live coral reefs can be seen around the southern islands further out in the Gulf.

The population of Kuwait now exceeds one million and is largely concentrated in the urban area surrounding Kuwait City. The remaining old-established centres of population are Fahaheel, Jahra and the oil town of Ahmadi. As is typical of coastal deserts, all the major settlements are within a few kilometres of the sea. This is simply because

Barchan sand dune. Umm Niqa and parts of the Wadi Al-Baten are the only areas where these crescent-shaped sand dunes are found. The convex side of the dune faces the prevailing winds and the steep-faced concave side is in the direction of travel. (VRK)

in the early days the land offered relatively few resources and the pioneers recognised the potential of the marine habitat. Indeed sea-faring and boat-building were among the most important economic activities to bring prosperity to the country. Modern highways have opened up much of the interior of the country and it is now possible to drive almost anywhere in Kuwait without difficulty. Together with the large population and its increasing demand for recreation, this has placed a greater strain on the desert community and those that remember the desert areas forty years ago now find it much impoverished.

Deserts have been defined as areas with extremes of temperature and an annual rainfall of less than 254 mm (10 inches). In Kuwait the summer temperature is well above 40 °C and the mean yearly precipitation a mere 100 mm. The effects of these conditions on the animal and plant life are exacerbated by the marked seasonal and daily variations. Daily temperature changes of up to 18 °C in winter are common. The highest temperature recorded in Kuwait was 51 °C in July 1978 and the lowest was − 4 °C in January 1964. Rainfall fluctuations are no less spectacular: the summer is almost completely dry with most of the rain falling in winter and spring. Annual rainfall also varies greatly; in 1964 a meagre 24 mm of rain was measured at Shuwaikh whereas 336 mm fell in 1954.

Heat and aridity are not the only characteristics of a sub-tropical desert climate; strong dry winds are also a feature. In Kuwait the north-westerly Tawz (or As-Somoun) winds prevail for nearly forty days during June and July. Together with the heat of the sun, these winds are responsible for the high

Stony desert. The topography of Kuwait is generally flat or undulating and large areas are covered by sand and gravel. In the north-east, shallow wadi systems, as shown here, indicate drainage patterns; elsewhere water drainage is internal (JNBB)

rate of water evaporation during summer and this loss of water further contributes to the difficulties faced by life in the desert.

Finally in this short account of Kuwait's weather extremes a mention must be made of dust- and sandstorms. A dust-storm is produced by a strong wind lifting thick clouds of dust particles thousands of feet into the air, effectively blocking out the sun. Sand, being much heavier, is rarely blown more than several feet off the ground. The abrasive force of the sand is well known and animals and plants either avoid such conditions or have suitable protection. In Kuwait dust- and sandstorms occur predominantly during winter and in June and July at the time of the Tawz.

With such extremes of weather it is difficult to believe that the Encyclopaedia Britannica could describe the Arabian desert as often being a lovely place. Other adjectives would seem more appropriate; inhospitable is one that could be applied in relation to the animal and plant life. Nevertheless it should be emphasised that these weather conditions are extremes and more usually the climate follows a relatively regular annual cycle. Animal and plant communities rely on this seasonal regularity to control their life cycles and it is therefore important to describe it.

The summer period is from June to September and is characterised by extreme heat during the day, especially during July and August when the skies are cloudless, the sun is at its highest and the days

Kuwait Bay. The 'sabkha' salt marshes and mudflats merge imperceptably into one another. The variable height of the two daily tide cycles and the variation in the height of the spring (highest) and neap (lowest) tides each month further exacerbates the difficulty of distinguishing where the land ends and the sea begins (DAC) ·

Opposite: **Dust-storm.** Clouds of dust extending several thousand metres into the air reduce visibility to less than 1000 m. Unstable air currents, high winds and dry, loose surface particles are the necessary conditions for dust-storms and hence they tend to occur predominately in summer. (MD)

Al-Khiran. To the south of Kuwait city sandy beaches with some rock outcrops and small coastal dunes predominate (KJM)

Mirage. The large shimmering lake at the foot of the Zor Ridge is in reality an optical illusion. Mirages are produced by bending of the rays of light from the sky as they travel through layers of air at different densities. (VRK)

are longest. Conditions are further exacerbated in June and July by the extensive dust-storms raised by the dry, hot north-westerly winds from the Iraqi desert. Thereafter the winds become light and variable in direction and the dust-storms diminish to be replaced in 'autumn' by only occasional dust clouds. There is no true autumn, however, for October is an extension of summer whilst November heralds the start of winter with the north-westerlies again beginning to invade the country. Blowing from the interior of Asia, the wind is cold and dry. Temperatures drop quickly to the winter levels and the transition from summer to winter may occur within hours of an active and thundery cold front. The annual rains continue intermittently until April, with most falling during the winter months, December to February. In some years dry and humid south-easterlies originating in the Red Sea control the weather and rain occurs along these fronts, sometimes as thunderstorms. Since the winds of winter are stronger than those of autumn, dust-storms again become a feature of the weather. The winter is cool and the nights can be unpleasantly cold with ground frosts, especially in January. The sun is low in the sky, the nights are long and the cloudless skies permit a rapid loss of the day's heat. Such conditions lead to the greatest difference between the highest and the lowest daily temperatures. Cloudy and damp weather will obviously minimise this difference.

March and April are the spring months and the weather is marked by sudden changes of temperature caused by variable wind direction. The difference between one day and the next may be as much as 15° C, the higher temperatures being produced by south-easterlies and the lower by north-westerlies. Strong south-easterlies also bring stormy weather, especially in March and April, and in April dust-storms may accompany the thunderstorms. Rainfall diminishes during April and north-westerly winds are responsible for dust-storms at this time. The temperature begins to climb rapidly as summer approaches and the annual cycle has come full circle.

In the following chapters the effects of topography and climate on the animals and plants will become apparent. From the seasonal flowering of plants and their seed's survival techniques to the behaviour of lizards as they move back and forth between the sun and shade, all are adaptations of living things to the environment in which they live.

Kuwait Bay. Looking across Ra's Kadhmah towards the Zor Ridge, the extensive tidal mudflats can be seen. Although several kilometres wide at low tide, many important marine organisms live in the zone of the mudflats adjacent to the shore line (CWTP).

Vegetation

By
Leon Corrall

Title page: **Borage herb,** *Moltkiopsis ciliata* (KJM)

The wealth or paucity of animals in an environment depends directly on the richness of vegetation. It is therefore only fitting that we should consider the plant community first in our study of Kuwait's natural history.

The area of which Kuwait forms a part has been defined as arid steppe or semi-desert, the characteristics of which are scattered, dwarf perennial bushes with annual grasses and herbs. Within this there are several community types based on the dominant species. In Kuwait, the two major types are those dominated by either 'Arfaj' *(Rhanterium epapposum)* or 'Hamdh', which can be one or other of the succulent shrubs known collectively as salt bushes. Different communities are also found where local topographical or geological conditions affect the overall pattern.

The factors common to all areas such as Kuwait are the obvious ones of high temperatures and

Picris saharae, 5 cm. One of the commonest of the desert daisies, this plant is found in sandy areas throughout Kuwait. The picture shows an area at the foot of the Zor Ridge in a particularly good year; the white flowers are *Anthemis deserti* (IW)

shortage of water, together with the less obvious but related problem of the high concentration of salts in the soil of some areas. Little rain means that there is minimal leaching of the salts from the soil. In locations where water is available such as at sewage outfalls or semi-permanent leaks, various plants flourish throughout the summer. For those plants that must survive without the deliberate or accidental assistance of man there are several methods by which they combat the rigours of a desert climate.

The perennials, plants that live for several years, must overcome the dual factors of water scarcity and the high evaporation rate experienced during the summer. One group of halophytic perennials, already referred to as the salt bushes, maintain leaves throughout the heat of the summer months, whereas others shed their leaves during the summer, sending out new growth with the autumn rains.

To be able to continue active growth throughout the hottest time of the year the salt bushes have to adopt the mechanisms found in succulents the world over. An extensive root system, disproportionate to the above-ground plant structure, is developed to tap water from a considerable area, and the leaf form shows adaptations necessary to avoid excessive transpiration and subsequent internal damage caused by wilting. The cuticle is thick and waxy and the stomata (breathing pores) are sunk below the surface of the leaf. By being circular in section the leaves are optimally shaped to reduce evaporation. The effectiveness of these mechanisms can be easily demonstrated by observing the amount of water released when the leaf of a salt bush is crushed. Tasting the sap will also show how these plants received their common name of salt bushes. Other halophytes are unable to contain the salt within their tissues but have developed the expedient of excreting crystalline salt from their leaves.

The group of perennials that are quiescent during summer are able to exist with less water, requiring only sufficient to avoid total desiccation during their period of inactivity. Without leaves, the woody members of this group give the appearance of being completely dead, but put out new leaves when refreshed by the autumn rains. However, the danger of transpiration in excess of water uptake is ever-present and the leaves are often small and inconspicuous and can be shed quickly, usually

Calendula persica, 15-20 cm. A common composite, *C. persica* blooms as soon as the seed has germinated. This particular specimen, only 3 cm tall, will grow considerably larger if its roots have found an adequate water source (LC)

Silene villosa, 10 cm. Abundant in sandy ground near the shore, this sweet-white campion is a member of the Caryophyllaceae (IW)

before the plant bears flowers. In extreme cases some plants produce no leaves at all and carry out photosynthesis through their stems. Such plants are sprawling twiggy bushes.

The non-woody perennials and the few biennials (plants that last for two years, the first season being devoted to growth with blooms being produced only in the second year) found in Kuwait retreat below ground level during the summer. As with the woody perennials, the autumn rains induce the return to active growth and subsequent blooming.

By far the most numerous flowers in Kuwait are the ephemerals, annual plants that have overcome the problem of climate by completely avoiding the harsh summer conditions. These annuals, which produce such a show of colour during the spring months and then wither in the heat of early summer, rely upon their seed for survival. The annual must flower and bear viable fruit to ensure propagation and, with flowering as its priority, produces blooms immediately upon unfurling its first leaves.

At this stage the tiny plants with showy flowers are at their most attractive. They resemble the alpine flowers in form for both must cope with the same problems of a short flowering season, strong desiccating winds and competition in attracting pollinating insects. The plants continue to grow during the flowering season when there is further rainfall, but much of the original attraction is lost as the flower size diminishes in relation to the rest of the plant.

To ensure propagation, the seeds of annuals must withstand high temperatures and be viable for at least twelve months. Commonly the presence of a chemical coating acts to inhibit germination. The seed will not grow until there has been sufficient rainfall to remove the chemical. This ensures that the seed is not wasted by germinating after a brief shower that has not provided enough moisture to sustain growth through to fruiting. Other seeds possess an inhibitor that must be removed by mechanical means such as would occur during transport amongst sand grains in flowing water. As removal of the inhibitor could also occur during wind transportation, it is possibly a device to ensure dispersal of the seed prior to germination.

The seeds of desert plants show all the well known mechanisms for dispersal, for example hooks and barbs to catch in the coats of animals and feathery parachutes for transportation by the wind. One interesting feature of the use of animals to aid seed dispersal is the somewhat fortuitous assistance rendered by ants. In hard, stony regions a patch of growth on the site of an ant hill will often be encountered. Here, where the ants' excavation has loosened the soil, plants can thrive in relative abundance.

The annuals, which emphasise dispersal of seed away from the parent plant, are the 'opportunists', forever trying to extend their range. It is amongst this group that the plants with most the extensive range and also the most erratic appearance are found. Such temporal dispersal is achieved through seeds with an extended viability and an irregular germination pattern, only some seeds germinating in any particular year. By contrast other annuals are 'conservative'. Having grown successfully in a given location, such plants restrict dispersal by failing to release seed until the next season's rain.

The general desert conditions are harsh, but annuals in particular exploit the availability of micro-habitats to the full extent. A micro-habitat is a very limited area in which the prevailing conditions differ greatly from those of the surroundings. This is well exemplified in the case of a community of annuals established around a larger bush. A small shrub will retain wind-borne sand to its leeward side and in this the seeds of many other plants successfully germinate. Without being in direct competition with the perennial shrub, whose roots are drawing water from a greater depth, the annuals benefit by the reduced evaporation from the partially shaded sand. They also receive the larger plant's protection from grazing by animals. The same principle often applies on the sides of wadis where a rock provides the shelter and inaccessibility that give protection from sheep and goats. Seeds and humus are often deposited together in such protected or low-lying situations by the action of the wind and rain and small pockets of relatively lush vegetation in an otherwise barren landscape are a common feature in Kuwait.

One group of plants comprising annuals and perennials but meriting a separate mention are the parasites. They are not directly dependent upon a source of water and their only requirement is the

Asteriscus pygmaeus. This inhabitant of stony areas has no stalk: the flower is fringed with leaves and the whole plant is flat to the ground. The dark objects in the centre are the previous year's seed pods (KJM)

presence of a host. Consequently they are not restricted in the same way as the free-living plants. Some parasites will grow only on one particular species or group of species, whereas others will use any plant indiscriminately.

Apart from true desert plants, there are several species that rely mainly or entirely on the assistance of man for their survival. These are the ruderals (plants of waste places), the weeds of cultivation or inadvertent water seepage. Some ruderals, however, will occasionally be found in the open desert after a heavy rainfall.

Before examining the flora of Kuwait in more detail, a brief mention of flowering seasons must be made. January, February and March are undoubtedly the best, but not the only, months for studying the flora of Kuwait. It is during this period that the annuals and many of the perennials are in full bloom, in good years transforming the seemingly barren desert into a carpet of colour. When the autumn rains are early and the winter temperatures not too low, flowers not normally seen until January can be found in November. Some of the ruderals are in flower virtually throughout the year and, of the true desert plants, several bloom in the hottest months. Self- and wind-pollinated flowers do not need to bloom in the spring when insects are present and it is during the summer heat that many of the salt bushes produce their inconspicuous little flowers.

The specific flora of Kuwait is described below in relation to regional variations of geology, climate and topography, but because of the dramatic effect of climate in this semi-desert area it must be realised that the boundaries are not rigid. Species of salt bush found in the mudflat region can also be seen 50 km from the coast.

Coastal Sand Dunes

The coastline of Kuwait can be split into two distinct types. North of Kuwait City the beach is gently shelving with mudflats, where it is hard to distinguish the tide line. To the south of the City, the beaches are sandy and the exposed nature of the coastline has given rise to the formation of small dunes.

Orobanche aegyptiaca, 17 cm. The only blue broomrape in Kuwait has a limited range; this particular plant, which was probably parasitising the *Erucaria hispanica* immediately behind it, was found in the coastal sand dunes to the south (KJM)

Zygophyllum coccineum, 70 cm. Found throughout the State but more frequently near the coast, this salt bush is the host for several parasitic plants (WAS)

The first growth encountered at the high tide line is often *Seidlitzia rosmarinus,* a shrubby, summer-flowering salt bush with long silvery-green cylindrical leaves which, when dried and pounded up, make a lathery soap. It grows to a height of about 1 m and, as is common with many of the Chenopodiaceae found in Kuwait, produces seeds whose papery wings are much more noticeable than the flowers. *S. rosmarinus* is also to be found in the sandy areas behind the mudflats of northern Kuwait. In fact it never occurs far from the sea, unlike another salt bush sometimes found with it, which may also grow in the gullies running down from the Zor Ridge. *Zygophyllum coccineum* (Zygophyllaceae) on first glance closely resembles *S. rosmarinus* but can be distinguished from it by its smaller size and its darker green ovoid leaves, which are usually branched. In May the creamy-white flowers that barely open appear looking very much like faded leaves.

*Heliotropium ramosissimum,*3 m. This member of the Boraginaceae has a woody stock that sends out new growth each year. It grows in rocky and sandy areas (KJM)

*Lycium arabicum,*1 m. Shrikes will often impale their victims on the sharp thorns that are a feature of this autumn-flowering plant (KJM)

Yet another of the producers of inconspicuous flowers is *Atriplex leucoclada,* a variety of Hamdh but atypical in that it lacks succulence. The genus *Atriplex* contains the common oraches found in Europe and *A. leucoclada* resembles them in form. An upright plant of about 50 cm with triangular greyish-green leaves, it produces spikes of small green flowers twice a year in spring and autumn. In addition to being found in the dunes, it also occurs in the sandy areas close to the sea in northern Kuwait.

Rocky sandstone outcrops in and behind the dunes are dominated by *Lycium arabicum (Lycium shawii),* a very spiny bush that grows up to 3 m in height. Shrikes often use it as a larder, impaling their prey on the sharp spines which are reputed to be slightly poisonous. White or violet trumpet-shaped flowers are produced in the autumn and the edible red pea-sized berries help in the plant's dispersal. The seeds inside an eaten berry are passed out of the animal unharmed in its droppings. The leaves, which are shed in the summer, are small and oblong. The very similar *Lycium barbarum* is found in the gullies of the Zor Ridge.

Another perennial of this region is *Heliotropium bacciferum (Heliotropium ramosissimum)* of the Family Boraginaceae. A tea and a poultice made from the dried pounded leaves of this plant are used by the Bedouin as a cure for snake bite. The plant's small white flowers are borne on a curled spike that unfolds like a spring as the flowers open.

Of considerable medical value, plants of the genus *Artemisia* yield vermifuges and stimulants as well as the active ingredient absinthe. *Artemisia herba-alba* is no exception, the herb being used as a vermifuge. The plant has woolly grey-green leaves that give off a fragrance when rubbed and small yellow flowers that open in late summer. This plant is less common than the preceding perennials but has a wider distribution, being found in the Wadi Al-Baten. Another rare inhabitant of the southern dunes, the Sea Lavender *(Limonium thouini),* has also been found in the Wadi Al-Baten and on the central reservation of the Airport road. This annual, a member of the Plumbaginaceae, produces a one-sided spike of yellowy-cream flowers in late spring. It has smooth light green leaves and the stem is winged.

Cakile arabica (Cruciferae) is a spring annual that bears mauve flowers, the four petals arranged in the characteristic cross common to the whole family. It is not restricted to the southern dunes, but also occurs in sand close to the shore elsewhere and on the Zor Ridge where it sometimes grows in profusion, perfuming the air with its sweet fragrance. Members of the broomrape family (Orobanchaceae) are root parasites and it is not always apparent which is the host plant. *C. arabica* is, however, probably the host for the broomrape *Orobanche aegyptica* which flowers at the same time as its host. Like all members of this parasitic family this attractive plant does not need to photosynthesize and therefore has no leaves or green pigment. Another spring-flowering broomrape with its small pale mauve flowers is *Orobanche cernua*, but the most spectacular of the broomrapes, parasitising salt bushes, is *Cistanche lutea*. Although found on the dunes it is by no means restricted to this region and can be found throughout Kuwait wherever its host grows. *Cistanche tubulosa* is another large broomrape but with a spike of showy bluish flowers which become yellow when fully opened. According to the nature of the host, this broomrape is either an annual or a perennial.

Cakile arabica, 50 cm. A fleshy, pleasantly scented member of the Cruciferae, *C. arabica* grows in sandy areas close to the coast. Pictured is a fairly young plant (KJM)

It is in dune formations that one first encounters many of the sand-dwelling species that occur over much of the interior of Kuwait. One of the first annuals to bloom is a small member of the Cruciferae, *Maresia pygmaea*. This minute plant, which is grazed by camels, has snowy white flowers that are tinged with mauve on the underside. Its thin branched or simple stem has a rosette of leaves at its base. Sometimes this plant can be mistaken for a close relative, *Savignya parviflora,* which also has light mauve flowers but in which the leaves are not confined to the basal rosette. In the Cruciferae, however, the seed pods are a useful guide in identification and those of *M. pygmaea* are long and thin, whilst those of *S. parviflora* are oval, short and flat.

Two of the Compositae that flower early in the spring and that can be found on dunes are *Anthemis deserti* and *Senecio desfontainei (Senecio coronopifolius). A. deserti* is a typical daisy with white ray florets and a disc of yellow tubular florets. *S. desfontainei,* a member of the ragwort genus, has both yellow ray and disc florets. The most impressive displays of *S. desfontainei,* how-

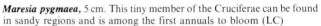

Maresia pygmaea, 5 cm. This tiny member of the Cruciferae can be found in sandy regions and is among the first annuals to bloom (LC)

ever, are to be seen by the roadside on the outskirts of Kuwait City where they sometimes form a continuous carpet of yellow. A similar member of the Compositae, *Calendula persica,* with yellow apical flowers is found in the low-lying areas behind the dunes. If its large dark green leaves are rubbed, the familiar marigold perfume of its garden relative can be smelt.

Anagallis femina is a very attractive little annual found in the same areas. It is a member of the primrose family (Primulaceae), closely related to the Scarlet Pimpernel and sometimes referred to as the Blue Pimpernel. As the common name indicates, its five-petalled flower is bright blue.

Two members of the storksbill family (Geraniaceae) seen in the dune area as well as the sandy areas of the interior are *Erodium deserti* and *Erodium ciconium*. They are similar in form, both having deeply dissected leaves and the familiar garden geranium-shaped flowers. Both these prostrate annuals are downy and produce the long

Cistanche lutea, 30-60 cm. With its large showy flowers this is one of the most impressive plants in Kuwait. It is a root parasite of various salt bushes and may grow up in open sand several metres away from its host (IW)

straight seed pods that give them their common name. *E. deserti* is the smaller and more common of the two having pale pinkish flowers and growing to about 15 cm. *E. ciconium* has larger mauve flowers, sometimes with purple veins, and grows to 40 cm.

The hollows behind the dunes where the rainwater run-off is greatest are probably the best areas to find the unmistakable *Asphodelus tenuifolius* in profusion. This annual member of the lily family (Liliaceae) produces a clump of hollow, rush-like leaves from the midst of which grows a spike of flowers. The individual blooms are pinkish-white with dark purple or brown veins and hang downwards like little bells. The seeds are used to produce 'igt', a kind of dried milk.

Of the nine species of *Plantago* found in Kuwait, *Plantago coronopus* is the one most easily identified. The flower spike is typical of all plantains (Plantaginaceae) but the leaves, which are all in the form of a basal rosette, have the distinction of being toothed. This is a good example of a 'conservative' plant and seeds are only released when conditions are favourable. High humidity is required to trigger a seed releasing mechanism in the capsule. Further, the seed coat swells and becomes mucilagenous in contact with water and sticks to the soil near the parent plant.

Another little annual that has a restricted range is *Bupleurum semicompositum*. It can be found elsewhere in the south besides the dunes, but apparently suitable habitats in the north are unoccupied. This inconspicuous member of the Umbelliferae lacks the familiar crown of flowers of other members of the carrot family. The genus *Bupleurum* is known as Hare's Ear but much imagination is needed to see any justification of this name in *B. semicompositum*. It grows to about 10 cm, has narrow linear leaves, and the flowers are small and brown.

Unlike the spring-flowering annuals, the perennial *Citrullus colocynthis* is in bloom almost all year round. The dune plants are, however, less impressive than those encountered in the gullies of the Zor Ridge and the Wadi Al-Baten, where an individual may cover several square metres. The creeping branched form and large bristly leaves are typical of the gourd family (Cucurbitaceae) of which *C. colocynthis* is the only representative in Kuwait. Its flowers are bright yellow and develop

Blue Pimpernel *(Anagallis femina)*, 10 cm. The Blue Pimpernel occurs in well watered sandy areas and is often found in the hollows between coastal dunes (KJM)

Asphodelus tenuifolius, 12-30 cm. An annual member of the Liliaceae, *A. tenuifolius* is relatively common and is found in sandy areas and at the edge of drain pans (WAS)

into spherical gourds about the size of a tennis ball. As the plant dies back, these dry out and remain scattered about the desert. A few seeds make a strong purgative but in large doses are poisonous and it remains a mystery why sheep rapidly gain weight when they eat the gourds.

Before leaving the dune formation and its vicinity, two grasses deserve mention. *Cynodon dactylon* is the common lawn grass in Kuwait but it can be found growing wild in low-lying areas. It is a creeping grass easily identified by its flower head of several separate spikes radiating outwards from the top of the stalk. *Aegilops triuncialis* is a tufted grass growing to about 15 cm; the flower head is distinctive in having bristles projecting outwards at a steep angle, giving the plant a spiky appearance.

Senecio desfontainei, 10 cm. A very common ragwort that can grow in profusion in sandy areas. This early flowerer, with its bright golden blooms, should not be mistaken for any other species (WAS)

Erodium deserti, 15 cm. The commonest member of the genus in the country, this widespread plant may even be found on central reservations in Kuwait City. The long seed pods that give the Family Geraniaceae its common name of 'storksbill' are well illustrated here (KJM)

Coastal Mudflats and Salt Marshes

The plants of the mudflats and salt marshes of north Kuwait are less widely distributed in other regions than are the plants of the dunes, if only because the conditions impose a degree of specialisation that renders many of them unfit to survive elsewhere. *Salicornia herbacea* is used as a fuel and is sometimes known as Glasswort because the ashes were once used as a source of soda in making soap and glass. It is a leafless, fleshy annual of the Chenopodiaceae found only on the mudflats and often below the spring high tide line. The seaward edge of the salt marshes is, however, more commonly dominated by another salt bush, *Halocnemon strobilaceum*. *Schanginia baccata (Suaeda baccata),* an annual salt bush with very fleshy linear leaves is also restricted to coastal areas but does not tolerate such a highly saline environment. It produces a dense spike of five-segmented green flowers that look like tiny green balls. It grows to 1 m and is in bloom in mid-summer. Two other typical salt bushes having succulent leaves and producing tiny flowers in summer are *Salsola baryosma* and *Suaeda vermiculata*. The flowers of the two plants resemble each other, but those of *S. baryosma* develop into papery winged fruits and those of *S. vermiculata* into naked seeds.

The numerical dominance of the salt bush in this area is somewhat offset by the presence of *Nitraria retusa* (Zygophyllaceae) and the Dwarf Tamarisk (*Tamarix passerinoides (Tamarix aucherana)* Tamaricaceae), which must be amongst the largest of Kuwait's indigenous plants, growing to several metres. They tend to trap wind-borne sand forming a small dune around them through which they continue to grow until a considerable 'hummock' is formed. When the bush is killed by cutting or over-grazing the dune is quickly blown away. *N. retusa* is a very strong thorny bush with slightly fleshy grey-green triangular leaves. It produces spikes of off-white flowers in late spring, which develop into hanging clusters of bright red ovoid berries. *T. passerinoides* has coarse, branched linear leaves having the ability to exude salt, and the flowers, which can be found in spring and autumn, are large and pink in small spikes. Both

*Halocnemon strobilaceum.*Often submerged by the tide, this low straggling bush shows lush growth in summer and flowers in September and October (DAC)

Nitraria retusa, 1-1.5 m. This thorny bush, around which sufficient sand may accumulate to form a considerable hummock, is often found growing with the Dwarf Tamarisk. *Tamarix passerinoides (T. aucherana).* The fruit, shown here, appears in May (LC)

these plants are good wind breakers and another Tamarix, *T. aphylla,* the Salt Cedar Tree was formally cultivated in the gardens of Jahra for this purpose and to provide roof timber. It has also been used in the government's afforestation programme round Kuwait City.

In the salt pans between the two bushes may sometimes be found one of the smallest plants. *Frankenia pulverulenta* is another plant that avoids high salt concentrations in its tissues by actively secreting salt through its small oval leaves. This plant, which bears the English name of Annual Sea Heath forms a dense mat of vegetation that lies flat to the ground. The small and star-like pinkish flowers appear in late spring.

In bloom slightly earlier, but in the same habitat, is the annual *Mesembryanthemum nodiflorum* (Aizoaceae) This has fleshy green cylindrical leaves and the same creeping form as *F. pulverulenta.* The flowers, which are similar to the cultivated mesembryanthemum, are white and yellow and resemble a daisy flower at first glance, although in no way are they related. Both the *Frankenia* and *Mesembryanthemum* are halophytes and are not found far from the coast.

Mesembryanthemum nodiflorum, 25 cm. A dwarf succulent growing in semi-saline environments close to the coast, *M. nodiflorum* belongs to the Family Aizoaceae but may initially be mistaken for a member of the Compositae (WAS)

Convolvulus oxyphyllus, 60 cm. In summer this plant resembles Arfaj *(Rhanterium epapposum)* and normally grows in sandy areas close to the sea. The specimen illustrated, however, was found at the edge of a gully in the Zor Ridge (LC)

One plant that is not common in the dunes of the south but that is most prolific in the very similar sandy areas behind the salt marsh is *Convolvulus sericeus* (Convolvulaceae). It is a very handsome upright perennial with soft downy grey-green leaves and large, pink trumpet-shaped flowers that are produced in late spring. Another convolvulus sometimes found with it is *C. oxyphyllus,* which has smaller greyish leaves and smaller white or pale pink flowers. Whereas *C. sericeus* dies back during the summer, *C. oxyphyllus* merely sheds its leaves and remains as a twiggy shrublet.

Sandy Desert

The bulk of Kuwait's flora is to be found in the interior of the country and, for botanical purposes, non-coastal Kuwait can be roughly divided into areas of sand and hard gravelly plains, with local topographical features that create specialised habitats. The flora of sandy areas is consistent throughout the State as is that of the gravel plains. Only when a species has been noted as having limited range will geographical locations be mentioned. The specific topographical features will be considered separately.

Desert areas with moving sand dunes are only to be found at Umm Niqa in the north and on the floor of the Wadi Al-Baten, but dune-less sand covers a large expanse of the country. Open sand predominates to the south of Kuwait City, along the foot of the Zor Ridge in the north-east and in the beds of wadis throughout Kuwait.

The dominant perennials of the sand are *Rhanterium epapposum* (Compositae) and the ubiquitous salt bushes. *R. epapposum* is a dwarf bush that grows to about 1 m with small yellow daisy flowers and is an excellent food for camels and sheep. This bush is widely distributed throughout Arabia and has been referred to in many old writings and sayings. It burns fiercely to produce a very hot fire and, before the advent of oil was the main source of fuel. It has silvery branches that remain bare throughout the summer, its small green leaves appearing in the autumn or early spring before the plant blooms in April.

Arfaj *(Rhanterium epapposum)* In April, at the end of the spring rains, these fragrant flowers appear in profusion covering the parent bush in a golden mantle. Kuwait has adopted this flower as its floral national emblem (RH).

Arfaj *(Rhanterium epapposum)*. 1 m. Providing food for domestic animals and firewood for the herdsman, this perennial bush fulfilled an important role in the nomadic Bedouins' life (RH).

The salt bush *Haloxylon salicornicum (Hammada elegans)* is also valuable grazing for camels and covers extensive tracts of country. It grows to about 1 m, has noticeably jointed leafless stems and produces minute flowers in late summer. The plant is at its most attractive in the autumn when the seeds have developed their papery wings which fall at the onset of colder weather and are often seen among the cargo of the ant caravans.

Also grazed by camels and very similar to *H. salicornicum* is the less common plant *Anabasis articulata*. It is stockier with tiny leaves at the joints, grows to the same height, has similar minute flowers but vertical instead of horizontal seeds.

A third salt bush of the Chenopodiaceae, which is abundant in localised areas, is *Cornulaca leuca-cantha*. This has dark green leaves that end in a spine and lack the succulence of other salt bushes. The tiny yellow flowers do not produce winged fruit.

Of the small annuals frequenting the sandy area probably the most conspicuous in their abundance and variety are the desert vetches. The following members of pea family (Leguminosae) are all spring-flowering annuals. After the autumn rains the leaves of *Lotus pusillus (L. halophilus)* are among the first to show. This plant has a single yellow flower that develops a long straight pod and has trifoliate leaves. Growing with it may be *Trigonella stellata, Trigonella anguina* and *Hip-pocrepis bicontorta,* which are all yellow legumes. *T. stellata* has a dense cluster of tiny flowers that form a knot on the prostrate stalk of the plant, while both *T. anguina* and *H. bicontorta* produce a crown of flowers held upright. The two *Trigonella* possess trifoliate leaves whilst those of *H. bicontorta* consist of several small leaflets. The seeds of *T. anguina* are sweet scented and can be used to give flavour to musty hay. The genus *Hippocrepis* is remarkable for the shape of seed pods produced. Although differing in form from one species to another they are consistent in developing a bizarre twisted and/or distorted pod and *H. bicontorta* is no exception: its pods are twisted into a ring and have semicircular notches.

Another genus that has noticeable seed stages is *Medicago*. In this group the pods are spherical, or nearly so, and often spiny, as in the yellow-flowered *Medicago ascheroniana,* and will stick to

Opposite: ***Haloxylon salicornicum,*** 1 m. This is the commonest of the salt bushes of the interior and often covers large areas of country. The large winged fruits seen here develop from inconspicuous flowers and may vary in colour from pink to pale yellow (WAS)

Hippocrepis bicontorta. The presence of seed pods allows this plant to be easily distinguished from other small yellow legumes. The pods have semi-circular notches and become twisted into an unmistakable ring shape (IW)

43

the wool of animals. Another valuable grazing plant in the same community is *Ononis serrata* which also has serrated leaves but a two-colour flower, the wings being violet and the standard white.

Growing in the same locations are several species of *Astragalus*. Members of this large genus all have pinnate leaves consisting of up to 15 pairs of leaflets. The flowers vary in colour, although mauve and white predominate in Kuwait, and are either single or in small clusters. At first acquaintance it is helpful to find plants with both flowers and seeds, as the pod shape is useful for identification. *Astragalus annularis* has either one or two mauve flowers producing a purple spotted pod that curles back to form an almost perfect ring. The white-flowered *Astragalus bombycinus* forms large fat pods that, like the rest of the plant, are covered with a fine down, whilst *Astragalus schimperi* has small clusters of white or mauvish flowers that develop into a star-shaped group of pods. *Astragalus peregrinus* has relatively large white flowers and the seed pods are straight or only slightly curved and deeply divided to resemble a double-barrelled shotgun. The whole plant is more robust than those previously mentioned and, although found in the open sand, appears to do better in the drain pans and is often found in iris beds.

Astragalus schimperi. The tight knot of seeds clustered at the centre of this plant, one of the commonest of the small spring-flowering vetches, is where the first flowers bloomed immediately on germination (KJM)

Alhagi maurorum, 20 cm. Known as camel thorn, *A. maurorum* is in flower throughout the summer. The flowers grow from modified stalks that resemble spines (ANHG)

Astragalus spinosus is a very different plant to the preceding ones and does equally well on sand or gravel. Sometimes called camel thorn it is so very spiny that no camels or sheep will eat it. A perennial bush, it grows to 1.5 m and produces white flowers shortly after the first autumnal rains.

Before leaving the Leguminosae there is another perennial that is known as camel thorn. This is *Alhagi mannifera (Alhagi maurorum)* and it probably better deserves the title because, although young plants may be found in the desert, it is rare for them to survive the attentions of grazing animals. One's best chance of seeing this plant is on the central reservation of dual carriageways within the City. *A. mannifera* is a very spiny plant whose crimson flowers grow straight from the spines. The insignificant leaves are shed before the plant comes into bloom which is from mid-May onwards.

The family with most members, both in Kuwait and globally, is the daisy family, Compositae. A few have already been mentioned but several more are to be found in the sandy regions. *Aaronsohnia factorovskyi* is an early spring flower that lacks ray florets, merely having a yellow disc. It is used in the manufacture of 'igt' and when eaten has a peppery taste. It is common throughout the country as is *Picris saharae (P. babylonica)*. This latter plant, which is not restricted to sand, has only ray

Astragalus bombycinus. The downy inflated seed pods of this common little desert legume distinguish it from other members of the genus *Astragalus* (WAS)

Aaronsohnia factorovskyi, 15 cm. Whilst this particular specimen was found in a pocket of sand between rocks, the plant is more frequently seen in well watered sand gullies (IW)

florets, which are tipped with brown. Less common than *P. saharae* but widely distributed is *Koelpinia linearis*. This also has only ray florets but is easily identified by its very fine grass-like leaves and bunch of curved barbed seeds.

The genus *Launaea* has five representatives in Kuwait; all are yellow and have only ray florets. Two are frequently found in sandy areas and, like the last three Compositae, are good for grazing. *Launaea angustifolia (Launaea arabica)* has dark-centred flowers whereas *Launaea nudicaulis* can be recognised by its rosette of reddish tinged leaves and banded stem which is devoid of leaves. Unopened flowers hang downwards and are striped.

Although yellow predominates among the Compositae one of the commoner members of the family, the desert thistle, *Carduus pycnocephalus,* has mauve flowers. It is unmistakable being the only true thistle found regularly all over the sandy regions. It will commence flowering when only 3 cm high but can grow up to 1.5 m in good years. Another little composite, *Atractylis flava (A. carduus),* has prickly blue-green leaves but disappointing flowers. In May only a small display of fawn florets are opened in the top of the large egg-shaped flower head.

Scabiosa olivieri, a flower that at first glance may be taken for a composite, in fact belongs to the teasel family (Dipsacaceae). This plant grows to about 25 cm, has branched stems with few leaves and bluish-mauve flowers. Although widespread it is never abundant.

Brassica tournefortii (Cruciferae) is a common member of the genus *Brassica* in Kuwait and is good grazing for camels and sheep because it keeps growing for a long time. It has a tall branched stalk (up to 1 m) bearing minute yellow flowers. When dead the plant becomes uprooted and is blown about by the wind, like the famous tumbleweed of North America, thus aiding seed dispersal. Another yellow crucifer is *Schimpera arabica* which, because of its hot taste is avoided by animals. This is more leafy and has larger flowers, although the plant itself seldom exceeds 30 cm. Examination of the seed pods for identification is again useful to distinguish between the two similar crucifers *Torularia torulosa* and *Carrichtera annua*. These may be found together although the latter more often occurs in pockets of

Koelpinia linearis, 10-20 cm. Lemon-yellow daisy flowers develop into these curved seed pods. The grass-like leaves and seeds at once distinguish the plant from other yellow-flowered members of the Compositae (KJM)

Reichardia tingitana, 15 cm. There are many yellow Compositae in Kuwait to confound the amateur botanist. This spring-flowering annual grows in sandy regions and may be identified by its deeply cut, downy leaves, its prostrate form and the dark centre of the flower (WAS)

sand in rocky areas. Both are spring annuals with small white flowers but very different seed pods. *T. torulosa* produces a long thin seed pod that curls up to form a ring whilst *C. annua* has a round pod with a noticeable lip. A large conspicuous member of the Cruciferae found in sand and on gravel is *Malcolmia grandiflora*. In years of heavy rainfall this can carpet areas of north Kuwait with its mauve flowers that, on close examination, reveal each petal to be 'two-tone' in colour. This helps distinguish it from the next species if no seed has been formed. *M. grandiflora* grows up to 75 cm and develops long thin curved seed pods. Of far more limited range than *M. grandiflora* is *Horwoodia dicksoniae,* which is at its most abundant in the Manaqish area. *H. dicksoniae* has a single-hued mauve flower and produces very

Launaea mucronata, 30 cm. All the *Launaea* in Kuwait are yellow and have only ray florets. This perennial herb of the sandy desert is grazed by camels and sheep (KJM)

Desert Thistle *(Carduus pycnocephalus)*, 3-150 cm. The exceptionally large specimen pictured here was found at the edge of a gully in a year of plentiful rain. A flower may be produced, however, when this thistle is only 5 cm high (KJM)

distinctive short and fat discus-shaped seed pods. If Kuwait should ever adopt a national flower this would be a strong contender. It was first collected here by Dame Violet Dickson and bears the specific name 'dicksoniae' in honour of her field work in the area and the discovery of this plant in particular.

One of the earliest flowers to put forth leaves is the dwarf mallow *Malva parviflora*. This has toothed, semi-circular edged leaves which are eaten as a vegetable and tiny five-petalled mauve flowers that fade to white with age. The leaves also have a variety of medicinal properties ranging from treating headaches to skin eruptions.

The Rosaceae family has but a single representative in Kuwait. *Neurada procumbens* is a prostrate annual with grey-green triangular leaves and

Atractylis carduus, 20 cm. This member of the Compositae is to be found in sandy regions. Despite its prickly appearance it is eaten by camels (LC)

Brassica tournefortii, 60-100 cm. Dead and uprooted plants of this very common species may often be seen blowing across the desert (WAS)

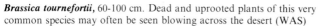

Schimpera arabica, 30 cm. The Family Cruciferae is well represented in Kuwait and *S. arabica,* which grows in sandy areas, is one of its commonest members (KJM)

Horwoodia dicksoniae, 18-25 cm. This species, first collected by Dame Violet Dickson, grows in sandy areas particularly in the south of the country. The characteristic seed pods can be seen to the left of the centre of the picture (KJM)

Dwarf Mallow *(Malva parviflora),* A representative of the Malvaceae in Kuwait, this mallow is very common. It is one of the first plants to grow after the autumn rain and thrives in well watered, low-lying areas. Its round flat seeds give rise to the Arabic name of 'khubbaiz' meaning 'bread' (KJM)

Malcolmia grandiflora, 75 cm. An annual common on dry sandy ground, this plant has long, thin seed pods that curve up as they develop (WAS)

inconspicuous greenish-white flowers and bears little similarity to its garden relatives that give the family its name. The most noticeable feature of the plant is its large round seeds that present an array of barbs to catch the feet of any grazing animal unwary enough to tread on them. The young plant sends out its shoot from the centre of the seed, which can still be found intact even when the plant has attained considerable size.

Although the Umbelliferae or carrot family has some half-dozen members in Kuwait, only one is commonly found. This is *Anisosciadium lanatum*, which has the finely dissected feathery leaves frequently encountered in the family and the usual crown or umbel of tiny white flowers. The seeds form a tight hard mass and are barbed.

A very common annual member of the sandy area flora is *Arnebia decumbens* (Boraginaceae), well known to the Bedouin ladies who rouge their faces by rubbing with freshly extacted roots or the juice squeezed from them. It is a light green plant with hairy leaves growing to about 15 cm. The bright yellow, star-shaped flowers come into bloom early in spring. Another member of this family, also inhabiting the sand, is *Moltkiopsis ciliata (Lithospermum callosum)*, a very hairy plant with small leaves and pink stems It is particularly common in the south where it may carpet areas of loose sand. The flowers are fairly small and vary in colour from white to purple, often all on the same plant.

Silene villosa (Caryophyllaceae), a showy white campion, is most abundant in this area. This sweet-scented annual has relatively large flowers with broad petals and blooms at night. Its close relative *Silene arabica* has fewer flowers and narrower petals. Another relative but one that has a very different form, *Paronychia arabica*, is prostrate and its inconspicuous flowers are virtually hidden by large papery bracts.

Two attractive members of the Scrophulariaceae or foxglove family found in sandy areas are *Linaria micrantha* and *Linaria simplex*, which both possess miniature snapdragon-like flowers. The former grows to about 8 cm and has large grey-green leaves and purple flowers. *L. simplex* is slightly taller, has fine linear leaves and bright yellow flowers.

Anisosciadium lanatum. This annual of the stony regions is the commonest member of the Family Umbelliferae in Kuwait. It develops a head of compact barbed seeds and so bears the Arabic name 'bis baas' or 'mother of teeth' (KJM)

Arnebia decumbens, 15 cm. One of the commonest of Kuwait's desert plants, this small, yellow-flowered member of the Boraginaceae blooms early in the season (WAS)

Linaria simplex, 30-40 cm. A member of the Scrophulariaceae, this annual of sandy areas closely resembles the toadflax common in Europe (WAS)

Paronychia arabica. The papery bracts around the small flower give this prostrate member of the Caryophyllaceae a silvery appearance (KJM)

Silene arabica, 15 cm. Early morning is the best time to see this annual whose flowers are fully open at night to attract night-flying insects (WAS)

Moltkiopsis ciliata, 15-20 cm. A spring-flowering annual, this bristly member of the Boraginaceae grows in sandy regions and, particularly in the south of the Country, can cover large areas to the virtual exclusion of other species (KJM)

There are three true poppies, all of the genus *Papaver,* found in Kuwait but not as frequently encountered as their relative *Roemeria hybrida.* However, the genus *Roemeria* is distinguished from *Papaver* only by seed-pod construction, and when in flower *R. hybrida* will easily be identified as a poppy. It has deeply dissected leaves and violet flowers that are best seen in the early morning because, if there is any wind, the petals soon drop.

Euphorbia isthmia, 30 cm. In common with other members of the genus, *E. isthmia* produces a milky latex when damaged. This small spurge can be found throughout the State (KJM)

Opposite: **Rumex vesicarius,** 20 cm. Distinguished from *Rumex pictus* by its fleshy leaves and unmistakable pinkish-red seeds, *R. vesicarius* is the commonest of the five members of the Polygonaceae family found in Kuwait (KJM)

Cynomorium coccineum, 30 cm. Resembling a fungus more than the true flower that it is, this strange-looking plant parasitises various salt bushes and thus lacks the green leaves necessary to produce its own energy (WAS)

The sorrels are members of the genus *Rumex* in the dock family (Polygonaceae). *Rumex vesicarius* has inconspicuous flowers that develop showy winged fruits brightly tinged with red and clearly veined. The fleshy triangular leaves can be eaten as a salad vegetable as can those of another common sorrel, *Rumex pictus.* The long white carrot-like root of *Emex spinosus* is also edible and the plant resembles *R. vesicarius* but has a prostrate form and spiny seeds. It is a very common plant often found supporting caterpillars of the Striped Hawk Moth.

Globally, the Family Euphorbiaceae is one of the largest, providing the African continent with many of its desert succulents. The five members of this family found wild in Kuwait are all herbs with inconspicuous flowers. One of the most abundant is *Euphorbia isthmia,* which has narrow leaves and grows up to 30 cm. It produces large seed pods and can be found in gravelly areas as well as on sand. Another member of this family worthy of note is *Chrozophora hierosolymitana (Chrozophora verbascifolia),* found in sand or in drain pans. This plant grows to 30 cm, has large grey-green woolly leaves and small yellow blooms that are out during the full heat of summer. The plant dies back when most others are beginning their cycle.

Cynomorium coccineum parasitises salt bushes both in sandy areas and elsewhere. Lacking leaves and bracts it has a remarkable appearance, rising straight from the ground to resemble a club-shaped fungus. Although it is a mild purgative its taste is enjoyed by many children.

Gravel Plains

Located mainly in the north and west of Kuwait, the expanses of hard gravel plains probably equal the sandy regions in total area. They are frequently broken by areas of accumulated sand with occasional drain pans or 'playas' of finer silty clay deposits. In the spring and early summer, the dominant growth of these gravelly plains is the grass *Stipa capensis*. It covers large areas and forms a continuous carpet of meadow-like growth. It is amongst this grass that most of the following species are found.

Two conspicuous members of the Family Cruciferae found in the gravel areas and also in the rocky scree of gullies are *Diplotaxis acris* and *Diplotaxis harra*. The two are almost identical in form having soft green foliage resembling cabbage leaves and growing up to 25 cm, but are easily distinguished because *D. harra* has lemon-coloured flowers whereas those of *D. acris* are purple. The displays of the latter in the Wadi Al-Baten can be very impressive when they cover large tracts and perfume the air.

Diplotaxis harra, 25 cm. This second member of the genus to occur in Kuwait has very different flowers from *D. acris*. Moreover, the seeds of *D. harra* hang down whereas those of *D. acris* are held upright, enabling these two similar plants to be easily distinguished (KJM)

Diplotaxis acris, 25 cm. Seen here growing in the stony ground bordering the Wadi Al-Baten, this plant, in years of heavy rainfall, will cover the whole area. The bitter leaves of the Cruciferae are sometimes eaten as a vegetable (KJM)

Another of the Cruciferae, *Matthiola longipetala,* can be found in the same area. This plant will grow to 40 cm and has narrow leaves clasping the stem.

The flowers are bi-coloured, the centres being creamy and the bulk of the petal reddish. Unlike the preceding three annual members of this family, *Farsetia aegyptia* is perennial, forming a small bush, which in summer somewhat resembles a grey Arfaj bush. The leaves and even the flowers are a greyish-brown. The seeds are oval and the plant is most commonly found on the crest of the Zor Ridge.

Two of the lily family (Liliaceae), *Dipcadi erythraeum* and the Star of Bethlehem, *Gagea reticulata,* are common in hard stony regions. Both are bulbous plants and those of the former are juicy and sweet to eat. *D. erythraeum* produces only two

Star of Bethlehem *(Gagea reticulata),* 8 cm. Fairly common in stony and rocky areas, this bulbous plant blooms early in the season. The yellow flowers may occur singly or in groups on each separate stem (ANHG)

Matthiola longipetala, 40 cm. The wavy petals of this flower separate it from other purple and mauve members of the Cruciferae, it is found in gravel areas and is less common than others of the family, which typically form large, single-species stands (KJM)

Dipcadi erythraeum, 15 cm. A member of the Liliaceae, this plant occurs in small groups in areas of rock and gravel throughout Kuwait (WAS)

or three long linear leaves and a single one-sided spike of brown bell-shaped flowers, which are succeeded by large fruits. *G. reticulata* also produces few leaves which are even narrower and more grasslike. The brilliant yellow star-like flowers may occur singly or in groups on each separate stem. *G. reticulata* is fairly common but *D. erythraeum* is found less often.

The vast majority of the Leguminosae are sand-dwelling annuals, but one member of this family that prefers the rocky areas is *Onobrychis ptolemaica.* Its creamy flowers with their brown stripes are held in a vertical spike and the seed pods coil up to form an almost perfect disc.

The mint family, Labiatae, produces many of the herb plants used in cookery the world over. The sage genus, *Salvia,* has at least two representatives in Kuwait, neither resembling the garden sage except in flower construction. *Salvia aegyptiaca* is a small plant about 10 cm high having small light

Onobrychis ptolemaica, 30-45 cm. This plant grows in rocky areas throughout Kuwait and is related to the fodder crop sainfoin. The hairy discus-shaped seed pods can be seen on the right of the picture (KJM)

Salvia spinosa, 1 m. A large member of the sage genus but lacking the fragrance of the herb, *S. spinosa* is rather restricted in its range and is virtually confined to the Wadi Al-Baten (KJM)

blue flowers with darker blue markings. By contrast, *Salvia spinosa* has large, coarse basal leaves, grows up to 1 m and has white flowers. Unlike *S. aegyptiaca,* which can be found in gravel and rocky gullies throughout the Country, *S. spinosa* is virtually restricted to the Wadi Al-Baten and the stony areas of that vicinity.

The storksbills, Geraniaceae, are represented in these regions by *Erodium glaucophyllum.* This plant has undissected leaves, relatively large flowers and very long seed pods.

A plant that appears to prefer the stony desert, although not restricted to this area, is *Reseda arabica* (Resedaceae). This member of the mignonette family has a showy spike of cream and yellow flowers.

Of the four *Helianthemum* (Cistaceae) found in Kuwait, the one most commonly seen is *H. ledifolium.* The flowers of this bright yellow rock rose open at sunrise but close before noon and are larger and more showy than those of other members of this genus. Seeing these plants brings an added pleasure as they indicate the proximity of the delicious desert truffles or 'fuga' which, because they are buried, are otherwise difficult to find.

An interesting parasite found in areas of gravel and particularly common to the west of Subiyah is the dodder *Cuscuta planiflora* (Cuscutaceae). This attacks virtually any plant by means of its straggling stalks which, in the early part of the season prior to flowering, resemble a tangle of pink cotton draped indiscriminately over other vegetation. The flowers take the form of pink balls along the length of the runners.

Reseda arabica, 30 cm. A desert mignonette that inhabits gravelly areas, this plant is a spring flowering annual (KJM)

Erodium glaucophyllum, 25 cm. Of the several storksbills to be found in Kuwait, this one may be distinguished by its uncut leaves. It is most frequently found in the Wadi Al-Baten, particularly on gravel plains (WAS)

Fagonia bruguieri and *Fagonia glutinosa* are two members of the Zygophyllaceae that grow in gravelly regions. The flowers of both are very similar, being perfumed and having five-petalled violet stars. However, *F. bruguieri* grows in the form of a dense cushion about 10 cm tall with needle-like leaves and spines, while *F. glutinosa* spreads across the desert floor by runners and has oval leaves that are sometimes trifoliate.

Two very different plants are the perennials *Gypsophila capillaris* and *Scrophularia deserti.* They can grow to 1 m in height and often stand alone in the 'puffy' gypsum-rich soil in exposed places. *G. capillaris* is a member of the Caryophyllaceae and has delicate white flowers and small leaves. The whole plant is much branched. *S. deserti,* the Desert Figwort, is also a fairly bushy plant. It has grey-green leaves and small purple flowers. If one is familiar with the European members of this genus of the Scrophulariaceae, *S. deserti* is immediately recognisable.

Helianthemum ledifolium, 25 cm. One of the commonest and most attractive of the rock roses in Kuwait, *H. ledifolium* may easily be overlooked for, like many of the Cistaceae, its petals are readily blown off (WAS)

Fagonia bruguieri, 10 cm. There are three members of the genus *Fagonia* in Kuwait and their flowers are very similar. *F. glutinosa,* however, is less spiny and has a prostrate form (LC)

One of the more spectacular members of the gravel community and one with restricted distribution is *Echium rauwolfii*. This very bristly member of the Boraginaceae has large trumpet-shaped flowers that vary in colour from red to mauve to blue according to age. It appears to be restricted to the gravelly areas of the extreme west near Salmi and the Wadi Al-Baten.

This area is also the best for finding several of the rarer composites. *Carthamus oxyacantha* is a tall (70 cm) yellow-flowered, thistle-like plant with large yellowish-green leaves that bear many spines. It is in flower well into May. *Centaurea pseudo-sinaica* is similar but its spines are restricted to the flower head. The unarmed leaves are an identifying feature of this genus, which also includes *Centaurea bruguierana*. This is a much smaller plant growing to about 25 cm with pale mauve flowers and white stems. It is not restricted to the west of the Country, being also found in the Zor Ridge.

The Zor Ridge is also the habitat of *Asteriscus pygmaeus,* another composite that is at once identifiable by the fact that it has no stem at all. The bright, daisy-like, all-yellow flowers, fringed by leaves, grow straight from the rocky soil. *A. pygmaeus* is one of the plants that exercises control over dispersal by retaining last year's seeds in the dead flower head until the new season's rain releases them. Another member of the same family, *Gymnarrhena micrantha,* goes to even greater lengths to ensure its survival. Its conventional flower releases freely dispersed seed, whilst at the same time the plant produces a self-pollinating underground flower which guarantees continued existence in the location already known to be favourable. *G. micrantha* takes the same form as *A. pygmaeus*. It is sessile, having no stalk, and its compact heads of minute purple flowers are fringed by long, glossy leaves. These two plants can often be found together, but, as one would predict from their different mechanisms of seed distribution, *G. micrantha* is more widely spread than *A. pygmaeus.*

The drain pans referred to earlier can occur in either gravel areas or sandy areas. They can be natural basins, sometimes only a few inches lower than their surroundings, or they can result from man's activities such as road construction or gravel digging. In either case the net result is the same.

Gynandriris sisyrinchium, 30-45 cm. The iris beds are one of the most impressive botanical sights in Kuwait. Some areas, such as Umm Al-Rimam are covered with irises in the spring. A pure white flower may occasionally be seen among the blue ones but is only a colour variation of the same species (KJM)

Echium rauwolfii, 30 cm. A member of the Boraginaceae that prefers sandy areas, it is at its most abundant in the west of the country. This particularly robust specimen was photographed in a year of good rainfall (KJM)

Centaurea bruguierana, 25 cm. In common with others of the genus, this plant is a late flowerer and was in bloom in May when most other plants had died. The calyx spines that are characteristic of the genus are well illustrated here (ANHG)

Gymnarrhena micrantha. Another sessile plant, lacking a stalk and growing as a prostrate rosette. This form is most suitable for the exposed stony areas in which the plant occurs (KJM)

The declivity traps fine particles of soil, humus and seeds, which, together with the additional water received, make the drain pans fascinating ground for the botanist. The species encountered are not necessarily different from those found elsewhere but here they are at their most profuse and luxurious. One can find carpets of the little Blue Pimpernel *(Anagallis femina)* and various species of *Astragalus* and Compositae grow to many times the size of their relatives in the open desert. Without doubt, the most spectacular flower of the drain pans is *Gynandriris sisyrinchium.* This delicate little blue and white iris can occasionally be found elsewhere but is most impressive when seen in great beds. The Umm Al-Rimam depression should be visited by all who wish to see this flower at its best. Its blooms open in mid-morning, a time when many flowers are closing. A plant that grows only in drain pans in the Subiyah area is *Bellevalia saviczii*. This is a little creamy white hyacinth, a member of the Liliaceae growing to about 10 cm with dark glossy linear leaves.

Specialised Localities

Bellevalia saviczii, 10 cm. A bulbous plant of very limited distribution, *B. saviczii* usually occurs only in the drain pans or 'playas' of the Subiyah area, often among the irises. Only rarely is it seen elsewhere (WAS)

In the preceding coverage of habitats, reference has occasionally been made to specific areas. Some of these require further description. The area of the Zor Ridge, sometimes referred to as Mutlaa Ridge, is the lime-rich escarpment that runs along the north shore of Kuwait Bay. Its deep gullies and protected slopes offer a wide variety of micro-habitats, as is also true of the Umm Al-Rimam, which lies immediately to the north of the Zor Ridge. This is a large depression fed by gullies

Calligonum comosum, 2 m. Seen at its best in the Zor Ridge, this shrub has small white flowers that develop into the spiny red seeds shown here (WAS)

Hand of Mary *(Anastatica hierochuntica)*, 4 cm. Known as 'Kaff Mariam' in Arabic, this tiny plant has just dropped its flowers and in this state gives no indication of the source of its common name (WAS)

similar to those of the Zor Ridge. These two topographical features possess much the same flora as encountered elsewhere but are noted for the variety and profusion of growth. A few species, however, are more or less confined to the Zor Ridge and the Umm Al-Rimam. One such plant found on inaccessible gully slopes is *Calligonum comosum* (Polygonaceae), a twiggy bush with narrow leaves which, when dried and pounded can be used for curing skins. It has fairly non-descript white flowers but produces spectacular shiny, bright red fruit.

Ochradenus baccatus is also a bush and will grow to 2 m when in a protected site but otherwise suffers much from grazing, particularly by camels. This is a member of the Resedaceae and has a flower spike of the same shape as others of its family. Its flowers are bright yellow, the leaves small and linear and the fruit is a small fleshy white berry.

Another speciality of the Zor Ridge is *Anastatica hierochuntica,* a member of the Cruciferae with the English name 'Hand of Mary' and the Arabic

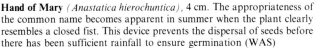

Hand of Mary *(Anastatica hierochuntica)*, 4 cm. The appropriateness of the common name becomes apparent in summer when the plant clearly resembles a closed fist. This device prevents the dispersal of seeds before there has been sufficient rainfall to ensure germination (WAS)

63

name 'Kaff Mariam'. It has small white flowers
that are virtually hidden by the large leaves and,
when the plant dies, its stalks fold inwards to
resemble a closed fist, hence its name. This is a
device to ensure that germination takes place only
after sufficient rain, as the fist unclenches to
release the seed when throughly saturated.

A plant found elsewhere but at its best in Umm
Al-Rimam is *Erodium bryoniifolium,* the largest
of Kuwait's storksbills. It has dark green deeply
dissected leaves, brilliant blue flowers and grows to
60 cm, forming dense patches of luxuriant growth
in good years.

The other area of great interest is the Wadi Al-
Baten. This major wadi forms the north-west
boundary between Kuwait and Iraq and access can
be gained only by obtaining permission at one of
the police posts on its southern edge. Many species
may be found here that do not occur anywhere
else in Kuwait.

Teucrium oliverianum is a violet-blue flowered
member of the Labiatae family that grows in
clumps in the runnels leading into the side gullies
of the wadi system. The leaves can be used to
prepare some tea and a medical douche for the
treatment of Basra fever (Malaria). Sometimes
Scorzonera papposa, an attractive member of the
Compositae with showy pink-mauve flowers and
long fleshy leaves, may be found with *T. oliverianum.* Also found growing in the sand in the
side gullies is another composite, *Echinops blancheanus.* This globe thistle grows to 1 m and has a
spherical head of pale blue flowers. The plant is
very spiny and its leaves are dark green with white
bands along the veins.

The dwarf bush *Anvillea garcini,* which grows to
about 50 cm, is another member of the
Compositae restricted to the Wadi Al-Baten area.
It has downy grey-green leaves, similar to those of
T. oliverianum, and produces yellow flowers, the
dried heads of which remain on the plant throughout the year. *Zilla spinosa,* a small spiny Hamdh
bush of about the same size, is found growing in
the gully bottoms only of this area. It is a member
of the Cruciferae having grey-green leaves and pale
violet flowers.

Anvillea garcini, 50 cm. Another plant restricted in its range to the side gullies of Wadi Al-Baten, this dwarf shrub retains its dead flowers throughout the year (WAS)

Scorzonera papposa. One of Kuwait's rarities, found only along the edge of the Wadi Al-Baten, the succulent tap root of this plant is sometimes eaten as a vegetable (KJM)

Echinops blancheanus, 1 m. The attractive green and white foliage of this globe thistle is well armed with spines. The plant's range is restricted to the gullies bordering the Wadi Al-Baten (WAS)

Teucrium oliverianum, 40 cm. This member of the Labiatae is found only in the west of the State, notably on the edge of the Wadi Al-Baten. It is a perennial, flowering in March and April (WAS)

It is in the vicinity of man that one finds the ruderals, and, though most of these 'weeds' are unspectacular, they are not without interest. *Portulaca oleracea* (Portulacaceae) is grown and sold as a salad vegetable but it is quick to revert to its wild form. Purslane is about 30 cm tall when cultivated, but its natural form is a prostrate annual with fleshy leaves, pink stems and yellow flowers. The success of this little plant can be gauged by the fact that it is found throughout Europe and can also be seen growing between paving stones in Bangkok and in the fields of California.

One of the most abundant of weeds is the Nettle-leaved Goosefoot, *Chenopodium murale.* Widespread throughout Europe, this plant can be found in Kuwait wherever sewage tankers discharge and particularly at sites of tree irrigation. It is a very leafy plant growing to about 35 cm and having small inconspicuous green flowers held in a spike. Often it forms a solid stand where other plants cannot tolerate the high nitrate concentrations.

Bassia eriophora, 15 cm. The seeds of this annual herb, which grows in areas irrigated by brackish water, closely resemble those of the cotton plant (KJM)

In some locations another member of the Chenopodiaceae, *Bassia eriophora,* can be found close to *C. murale.* Although it grows occasionally in the saline areas near the coast, it fares better in cultivated areas irrigated by brackish water. *B. eriophora* has soft downy leaves, grows to about 15 cm and produces tiny yellow flowers. In fruit it is unmistakable as the whole plant becomes covered with white cottony hairs.

Also in gardens irrigated with brackish water one may find *Cressa cretica,* a member of the Convolvulaceae. It attains a height of about 10 cm and has small white flowers and tiny leaves clasping the stem.

Two members of the Zygophyllaceae having potent pharmacological properties and found in waste places are *Tribulus terrestris* and *Peganum harmala.* *T. terrestris* is sometimes known as Caltrops, the mediaeval anti-cavalry device which, when scattered in front of a charging enemy, always landed with at least one of its many spikes pointing upwards. Indeed the seeds produced by the five-petalled yellow flowers are very spiny. The plant

Cressa cretica, 10 cm. A small creeping plant common on salty ground, *C. cretica* flowers in autumn and again in early summer (LC)

Zilla spinosa, 50 cm. This compact thorny bush grows among various Hamdh bushes only in the gullies of Wadi Al-Baten (KJM)

Peganum harmala, 55 cm. A member of the Zygophyllaceae, this perennial grows from a woody stock and occurs as a ruderal in Kuwait. Blooming in April, the specimen pictured was found among debris near Dohah (ANHG)

has leaves consisting of about six pairs of leaflets and is creeping in form. It is fairly common on central reservations throughout Kuwait City. In its urban habitats it blooms throughout the year but when occasionally found in the desert, it blooms in the spring.

Peganum harmala has a much more restricted distribution; favouring disturbed ground, it is sometimes found in areas excavated by gerbils. It forms a small shrublet about 55 cm high with fine leaves and an attractive white flower.

These brief descriptions are a somewhat arbitrary selection of less than a quarter of Kuwait's flora, but it is hoped that this has been enough to whet the reader's appetite and that he will now discover for himself that the deserts of Kuwait have far more botanical interest than at first appears.

Land Invertebrates

By
David Clayton

There are vast numbers of invertebrates in the desert but if one had to be chosen as a symbol of the desert it would undoubtedly be one of the Arachnida. This group contains the mites, ticks, spiders and scorpions and the choice of symbol would be between a scorpion (Order Scorpiones) and a wind scorpion or camel spider (Order Solifugae). Common desert creatures, they are both formidable nocturnal predators locating their prey principally by the sense of touch. They eat chiefly insects and spiders but any small animal may be attacked and devoured. Mortal combat could be one way to decide which should 'champion' the desert invertebrates but even here they

Black scorpion *(Androctonus crassicauda)*. Once firmly held by the clawed pedipalps, a victim has little chance of avoiding the scorpion's sting and is not released until all struggling has ceased (WAS)

are remarkably well matched. Contests between the two can go either way, depending on whether the scorpion can use its poisonous sting or the camel spider its enormous jaws. The poison will kill the camel spider within a few minutes and the scorpion can easily be crushed by its opponent's jaws. If the sting is severed in the initial attack the scorpion will surely fall prey to the solifugid. The camel spider can macerate its victim's body by passing it sideways to and fro through its jaws, and then suck out the body's contents. The voracious beast often continues feeding until its abdomen is so swollen that it can hardly move. A successful scorpion on the other hand grasps the moribund solifugid with clawed pedipalps and may take some considerable time to consume its victim.

One animal is as good as any other to eat, even another member of the same species, and both scorpions and the solifugids are cannibalistic, larger specimens usually eating smaller ones. Anyone who has kept a group of scorpions often finds himself after a time with one huge specimen and lots of bits and pieces. Cannibalism, however, is not confined to captive specimens and a scorpion interested in mating must be careful to find a partner with the same, rather than predatory, inclinations otherwise it may end up as a meal rather than a mate. Scorpion courtship takes the form of a dance in which the male grasps the female's claws in his. He then walks sideways or backwards whilst she follows. The 'dance' is really a search by the male for a suitable piece of firm ground onto which he can deposit a sperm capsule known as a spermatophore. He then drags his partner over it and, by lowering her body, she is able to pick up the spermatophore. The young are born alive as miniature adults and are carried around on their mother's back until they become independent after their first skin moult. Scorpions are unique in possessing paired comb-like sensory appendages called pectines beneath their bodies and it is possible that they are involved in detecting the correct substrate for successful spermatophore transfer during the courtship dance as well as in detecting ground vibrations.

In Kuwait there are at least two identified species of scorpion both belonging to the Family Buthidae, which are found in burrows and under anything that will provide protection from the harsh environment. The most conspicuous but not necessarily the most common species is the Black

Yellow scorpion *(Compsobuthus arabicus)*. Less commonly seen and usually somewhat smaller than its black relative, this scorpion is reputedly more venomous (WAS)

Camel spider *(Galeodidae)*. Sometimes called the wind scorpion because of its great speed, this has a formidable appearance with its leg-like pedipalps and huge jaws (DAC)

Scorpion *(Androctonus crassicauda)*. The remainder of the scorpions in Kuwait are a pale transparent green or yellow and are not, as is sometimes thought, young of the black species. Whilst they are usually smaller than their more conspicuous black relations, their venom is reputedly more toxic. It is here that the confusion over numbers arises for it is still not clear whether the yellow scorpions belong to two or more species.

If a scorpion has to be careful in the selection of a mate, the male camel spider has to be more so. Females are usually stronger and certainly more aggressive than the males, which will even flee from small struggling prey. The female is more tenacious, biting sooner and holding on for longer. The male courts his mate by stroking her to induce a sort of trance to enable him to accomplish the delicate task of mating without being eaten. With raised abdomen and folded legs the entranced and passive female is transported by the male for a short distance before being laid on her side to be further massaged on her underside. Lifting his abdomen he produces a spermatophore which falls to the ground. With one chelicera (jaw) he grasps the female's genitalia and with the other he inserts the spermatophore into the genital opening. He then holds the opening closed for a few moments before scurrying off to avoid possible capture. If the two should meet again within a few minutes, the female adopts the normal threatening attitude and her mate a normal male's response of running away. After mating the female becomes gluttonous for two weeks or so and then excavates a deep burrow in which the live young, still encased in their egg cases, are laid. They hatch out within a few hours but remain as dead for a further two weeks before moulting and becoming active as miniature adults. Good mother that she is, the female mounts guard over her offspring during this vunerable period. Surprisingly, nothing is known with any degree of certainty about the solifugid's life span or even about the number of moults and the time required to reach the adult form.

The camel spiders found in Kuwait belong to the genus Galeodes. They can sometimes be found underneath rocks or other heavy debris but usually live in long horizontal burrows, which are especially numerous where there are bushes and scrub. Being strictly nocturnal the solifugids do not emerge from their burrows during the day but as they are attracted to light after dark they are frequently found in houses in the more rural areas.

As is becoming apparent, males of predatory invertebrates are faced with difficulties when it comes to procreation and the spiders, the third group of arachnids, are no exception. Like the carnivores they are named after, the wolf spiders (Family Lycosidae) hunt down their prey instead of making webs, although the species found in Kuwait does use silk to line the burrow and to weave and bind the vegetation at its entrance. Whilst these spiders have simple one-facet eyes rather than the multifacet compound eyes typically associated with insects, they have relatively keen eyesight for detecting prey. They catch small insects by chasing them and then darting in and out to deliver telling bites with their strong jaws. When the prey is subdued they feed in the same manner as scorpions and solifugids, chewing the prey to a pulp and then sucking the juices through a mouth too small to admit any but the smallest particles. The male wolf spider often has strikingly adorned palps, which are used in a kind of sem-aphore to signal the female from a safe distance. He will not approach closely until she returns the signal to indicate her readiness to mate. Silk is also used by the female to spin a cocoon to carry the eggs on her abdomen. Hatched spiderlings stay in the cocoon until it splits when they move onto their mother's back, remaining there for several days.

Besides the Lycosidae, the Order Araneae (spiders) is represented in Kuwait by several other families although one of the most commonly seen 'spiders' is not a spider at all! The harvestmen or harvest-spiders belong to the Order Opiliones and are those short round-bodied arachnids having their eyes perched on top of the body. Their legs are very long and somewhat insecurely attached. Attempted capture often relieves the animal of a number of legs but even with eight to play with the loss of the second pair is fatal since they are the animal's nose, ears and tongue. With their un-quenchable thirst and poor powers of water con-servation they are restricted to the fringes of the desert and are more commonly seen in the home or the garden.

In terms of colour rather than size the most con-spicuous spiders of the desert are the jumping spiders (Family Salticidae). These are small squat

Wolf spider (Lycosidae). This spider is carrying her eggs in a silk cocoon suspended beneath her abdomen. Hatched spiderlings stay in the cocoon until it splits when they move on to their mother's back (WAS)

Opposite: **Wolf spider** (Lycosidae). Poised at the entrance to its burrow this spider rests after adding silk to the entrance (WAS)

spiders with broad square heads, large eyes and short thick legs. Their brilliant colouration rivals that of the insects. Keen eyesight enables them to stalk prey from a distance. During the search running may alternate with freezing but once the prey has been sighted the spider slowly stalks towards the intended victim unitl it is close enough to jump at and seize it. By contrast the crab spiders (Thomisidae) are sedentary animals with markedly cryptic colouration, so that even if these spiders are not hiding under stones or vegetation they are remarkably difficult to see unless they move. The crab spider lies in wait and seizes passing prey in its long powerful legs. The group derive their English name from the fact that they can run sideways (like a crab) or backwards.

The celestial place of the scorpion in the Zodiac and its place in mythology was probably inevitable but the place of the spider in Man's folklore is due to the cobweb (Agelenidae) and orbweb (Argiopidae) families of spiders attracting his attention. All spiders produce and use silk but the gossamer threads of a spider's web represent the crowning achievement in its use. Cobweb spiders make a variety of traps ranging from a funnel-shaped web to a triangular sheet with a tube at its apex in which the spider awaits its prey. In contast to the orbweb the silk is not adhesive and the spider relies on its speed to capture the hapless insect that falls onto the web.

Excellent predators that they are, spiders are subject to considerable predation themselves and have evolved all kinds of protective devices. Crypsis (camouflage) has already been mentioned and many hunting spiders build silken protective cells in which they rest when not hunting. The web advertises a spider's presence but the spider often hides close by or resides in the web only for short (hunting) periods. Even then some spiders manage to provide camouflage for themselves by adding narrow ribbons of silk to the web. Spines, un-pleasant flavour and scent are other devices used by spiders to deter predators. Some mimic the shape and colouration of poisonous or distasteful insects such as ants, wasps and beetles. Some even mimic scorpions but whether such mimetic spiders exist in Kuwait is not known.

The parasitic ticks and mites (Order Acari) com-plete the arachnids and in general are well adapted to desert living since they show astounding powers of water conservation when not attached to their

Crab spider *(Thomisus* sp.*)*. These spiders do not spin a web but ambush or stalk their prey. The bright colours provide good camouflage when the animal is hiding among flower heads (IW)

Opposite: **Jumping spider** (Salticidae). Commonly found in garden foliage, this keen-sighted spider actively hunts its prey and only makes webs as nests for overwintering or egg laying (ASDF)

Orbweb spider *(Argiope* sp.*)* Species of *Argiope* often camouflage their webs by adding white zigzag strands. With white marks on its body, the spider tends to blend into the design and become 'invisible' to predators (EJG)

Red velvet mite (Trombidiidae). The bright velvet-textured body has a clear aposematic function, serving to warn predators of this mite's unpalatability (CWTP)

host. One of the largest and most spectacular of Kuwait's mites, the giant Red Velvet Mite (*Dinothrombium* sp.), is not, however, especially resistant to desiccation and usually appears on the surface only after rain. The larvae are parasitic on grasshoppers but the free-living adults probably feed on other insects. The mite's body has the texture of velvet and the bright colour has an aposematic function, serving to warn possible predators of its unpalatability. This tactic of advertising one's own unpleasantness through bright colouration or even conspicuous behaviour is a common one adopted by many animals including insects: indeed the bees and wasps are probably the most famous example of this. Further, as mentioned earlier, harmless animals can also gain a measure of protection from predators by copying or mimicking such animals and some of these will be mentioned later.

Some indication of the problems facing invertebrate terrestrial animals under desert conditions has already been made but the problems and their solutions should be made more explicit. Clearly the most important danger faced by desert animals is water loss, which is more severe for small animals with their relatively enormous surface area. Scorpions, spiders, mites and many insects avoid becoming dried up by secreting a very thin impermeable wax layer on their cuticle. In ecdysis the new wax layer is even laid down beneath the old cuticle that is due to be cast off so that there is minimal water loss. The wax is also impermeable to oxygen and carbon dioxide and respiration is internal, taking place at the end of a branching tracheal system in insects and solifugids and in the lung book of other arachnids. In order to minimise respiratory water losses these systems are normally closed to the outside and opened only for removal of accumulated carbon dioxide. Excretion of uric acid by insects and guanine by arachnids also helps conserve water since both substances are extremely insoluble and nitrogenous waste matter is eliminated from the body in a dry state without water loss. Burrowing is widely developed amongst arachnids and insects and is of great importance to species that live in deserts. By burrowing, the animals are able to establish for themselves a micro-climate in which the conditions of temperature and humidity are much more favourable than those of the surface. Still, the animals sometimes must brave the surface and expose themselves to the full force of their environment's inhospitality.

They minimise its impact by having activity cycles geared to the most suitable time of emergence and become nocturnal (active by night) or crepuscular (active at twilight or just before dawn). Those that remain diurnal (active by day) often have higher basic tolerances to high temperatures and to desiccation than their nocturnal or temperate region counterparts.

For the most part these behavioural, morphological and physiological adaptations just described are essentially adaptations to life on land and are typical of arachnids and insects the world over. It is simply fortuitous that these adaptations have, so to speak, pre-adapted their bearers so admirably to the rigours of the desert environment.

Another mechanism used by many invertebrates to avoid unfavourable conditions is well illustrated by the only common land snail *(Eremina desertorum)* found in Kuwait. Molluscs of this species have been known to survive droughts of several years' duration in a state of suspended animation. In this dormant state, or diapause, growth and reproduction stop, the animal's life processes slow considerably and there is an increased resistance to heat and other unfavourable conditions. In summer large numbers of empty distinctive white shells of dead individuals are often found. Typically the snails confine their activity to the winter months when there is sufficient rain to bring them out of the diapause; during summer they remain inactive deep underground or under rocks.

Having established several generalisations concerning invertebrate adaptations to desert climes, let us now consider some of the exceptions. Crustacea found in deserts can be divided into two groups. The first are those that inhabit temporary pools of water and pass the remainder of the year as drought-resistant eggs. These animals are mentioned in the chapter on marine life but here we shall consider the second group of desert crustaceans. Woodlice are isopods belonging to the Suborder Oniscoidea and can only exist in moist or humid environments because they lack the water-proofed cuticle of other land invertebrates. Nevertheless, by burrowing by day and emerging at night and having the ability to absorb water from their surroundings they are able to survive in arid regions.

Centipedes or Chilopoda also lack the wax layer and are nocturnal, living in damp, dark places

Land snail *(Eremina desertorum)*. Empty shells are all that most people find of the land snail in Kuwait. Live animals spend the summer deep underground in a state of suspended animation (WAS)

Centipede (Geophilomorpha). Lacking a wax layer to the cuticle, centipedes are not well adapted to the harsh desert conditions. They are nocturnal and live in damp dark places (WAS)

under stones or in crevices in the ground. They are carnivorous and possess venom glands in their claws. The venom is rarely fatal to man but will cause considerable pain that may be accompanied by swelling of the affected area. There are several orders of centipedes and three are represented in Kuwait. That belonging to the Scolopendra can grow up to 20 cm and is pale yellow but can most easily be recognised by its 21 pairs of legs. The second centipede is much smaller and darker but has many more pairs of legs. The Geophilomorpha to which it belongs are long, worm-like centipedes having between 31 and 171 pairs of short legs. With only 15 pairs of exceedingly long legs, members of the third order of centipedes, the Scutigerimorpha, are also easy to recognise. Unlike other centipede orders they possess compound eyes and are very agile and active.

The ubiquitous presence of insects is as much a tribute to their adaptability as to their powers of flight. There is scarcely a place in the world that is not home to at least one kind of insect. The desert environment is no exception and provides a home for over three-quarters of the 32 orders of insects that comprise the Class Insecta. It would be neither practical nor useful to mention all these, let alone the families or species of which they are composed. The interested reader is directed to other sources and here only the more important, interesting or spectacular insects will be mentioned.

Migration is more commonly associated with birds but surprising numbers of insects also migrate.

Locust *(Anacridium melanorhodon)*. Species identification of grasshoppers is very difficult and this one is no exception. With its black and orange colouration, this species is very similar to the gregarious phase of the Desert Locust (KJM)

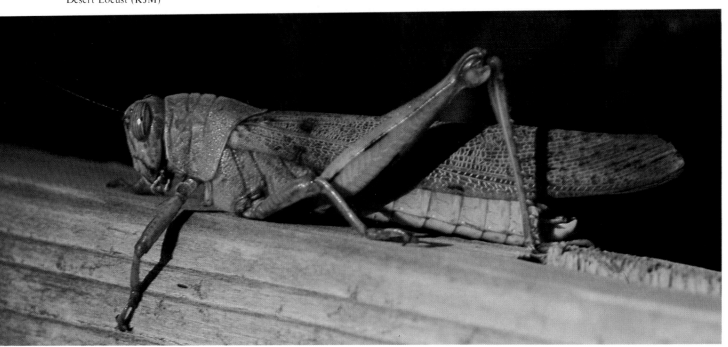

One that springs to mind is the locust and Kuwait is fortunate to be outside the normal range of the vast voracious swarms of these creatures, which do so much damage in their passing. Locusts migrate only during their gregarious phase, relying on the assistance of prevailing winds as do most other migratory insects. At other times they are solitary and behave much as other grasshoppers do. It is usually in this form that the Desert Locust *(Schistocerca gregaria)* is found in Kuwait.

The most famous of the migrant butterflies are the Painted Lady *(Cynthia cardui)*, the Red Admiral *(Vanessa atalanta)*, and the Clouded Yellow *(Colias crocea)*, all of which migrate north during the spring and south during the autumn. Butterflies such as the Long-tailed Blue *(Lampides boeticus)* are considered as irregular migrants and most others will show some migratory activity. The Painted Lady is the most common of the large butterflies seen in Kuwait and is found almost all the year round but in greater numbers in the cooler months. In December and January sharper coloured, locally hatched individuals appear.

Painted Lady Butterfly *(Cynthia cardui)*. Relying on the assistance of the prevailing winds, as do most other migratory insects, tattered specimens of this butterfly arrive in Kuwait during September and October to breed in the desert (ANHG)

Striped Hawk Moth *(Hyles lineata livornica)* on *Calligonum comosum*. At hatching this caterpillar is dirty white without pigmentation. The pattern of colouration and the horns develop later but the specific colours vary according to the environment (KJM)

Striped Hawk Moth *(Hyles lineata livornica)*. Feeding like a humming bird this moth hovers by the *Tagetes* flower and extends its proboscis into it (EJG)

Other butterflies found in Kuwait include the Plain Tiger or Indian Milkweed *(Danaus chrysippus)*, the Swallowtail *(Papilio demoleus)*, the Desert Small Blue *(Chilades galba)*, the Small Blue *(Cupido minimus)*, the Persian Skipper *(Spialia phlomidis)*, the Desert White *(Pontia glauconome)*, the Green-striped White *(Euchloe belemia)* and the Small White *(Pieris rapae)*. Previously there were only the desert plants to attract the Lepidoptera (butterflies and moths) but the cultivation of land in recent years has vastly increased the available habitat. Ahmadi especially suffers from the attack of these insects. Gardeners will awake to find their carefully tended young plants unaccountably dying. The culprits are caterpillars with a catholic taste in succulent and vulnerable young plants. Buried in the ground by day the larvae of such moths as the Turnip Moth *(Agrotis segetum)* and the Silver Y *(Plusia gamma)* emerge at night to do the damage. The latter, incidentally, is also a well-known migratory species. Even the Sidr tree *(Zizyphus spina-christi)* is not safe from the chomping jaws and can be denuded in the autumn by the hairy caterpillar of the moth *Thiacidas postica*. When ready to pupate, this caterpillar leaves the trees and buries itself in the ground where a loosely woven cocoon of its hair and sand is made. In a manner typical of many Lepidoptera it then lies dormant for some time, in this case until July or August when pupation occurs. The adults appear on the wing in mid-September to October. The caterpillar of this moth does not appear to have many enemies; birds will not eat them because of the irritating effect of the hair, which can also cause skin rashes in Man. The presence of hairs is a common defensive mechanism of caterpillars and one that can also assist in dispersal. Some hairy species roll up and are blown along by the wind. Other caterpillars rely on camouflage for protection. Hawk moths produce caterpillars with many different coloured forms. For example the Oleander Hawk Moth *(Daphnis nerii)* which is also found in Kuwait has green and brown forms. From the study of another species of hawk moth it seems that the colours are correlated with behavioural changes that render them cryptic. Should this first line of defence fail, the caterpillar can fall back on a secondary system designed to startle the predator. Swelling of the thorax and withdrawal of the head reveal an eye-spot that is normally hidden. The sudden appearance of this 'staring' eye is often sufficient to deter the predator

Moth larva *(Thiacidas postica)*. Birds usually avoid hairy caterpillars because of the irritating effect of the hairs in the bird's mouth and respiratory passages (ASDF)

from further investigation. The eye-spots on the underwings of otherwise drab moths have a similar function. Even the pupae have startle defensive mechanisms; an apparently lifeless pupa may start violent and disturbing movement when picked up. The Death's Head Hawk Moth *(Acherontia atropos)* pupa, which can be found in the soil of local gardens, also emits squeaks when it is touched and this is sufficient to intimidate all but the most persistent predator. Butterflies also show similar mechanisms. The Plain Tiger, as its second name Indian Milkweed suggests, feeds on milkweeds and may accumulate chemicals that cause vertebrate predators to vomit when the insect is eaten. The butterflies' distinctive patterning enables the predator to learn quickly to avoid them.

Locusts have already been mentioned and it is appropriate to consider here the remainder of the Orthoptera. These are the crickets and grasshoppers which appear in abundance on the vegetation that springs up after rains. As a substantial part of the food supply of many desert predators these omnivorous insects are an important element of

Striped Hawk Moth *(Hyles lineata livornica)*. The distinctive markings that give the moth its English name are clearly seen in this resting specimen (WAS)

Cicada (Cicadidae). The song of the male cicada is species - specific and serves to attract other members of the same species (WAS)

Oleander Hawk Moth *(Daphnis nerii)*. In common with other hawk moths, this species has different-coloured larval forms at different stages in its life cycle. The light phase is shown here (ASDF)

Silver - striped Hawk Moth *(Hippotion celerio)*. A dark phase individual is shown here on *Rumex vesicarius*. If crypsis fails the caterpillar has a second line of defence designed to startle the predator. Swelling of the thorax and withdrawal of the head reveal an eye-spot that is normally hidden (PRH)

Short-horned grasshopper (Acrididae). Common throughout the months of spring and early summer grasshoppers provide a welcome source of food for reptiles and birds (IW)

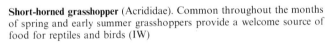

Oleander Hawk Moth *(Daphnis nerii)*. The pupae have a startle defensive mechanism; apparently lifeless pupae may start violent and disturbing movements if picked up (ASDF)

Opposite: **Plain Tiger Butterfly** *(Danaus chrysippus)*. The shell of the stalked chrysalis and the fresh, sharp colours of the insect show this to be a newly-hatched specimen (EJG)

Oleander Hawk Moth *(Daphnis nerii)*. The patterning of the sharply cut, narrow wings provides effective camouflage when the animal is resting on Oleander, its food plant (ASDF)

Short-horned grasshopper (Acrididae). Most species pass the winter in the egg stage, the eggs being laid in the ground (WAS)

the fauna. One characteristic of the group is the enlargement of the last pair of legs for jumping. These have been lost in the mole crickets *(Gryllotalpa* sp.) since they have become adapted for a subterranean life. The forelegs have become modified for digging and bear a strange resemblance to those of the mole. Most crickets are more often heard than seen and, in the cool of the evening, their songs and chirrups can be a delight to the ear. Grasshoppers and crickets have a variety of sound production mechanisms that all involve rubbing two parts of the body together. There are three main types of male song: the spontaneous song of sexually mature males, the wooing song when females are near and the rival duet of males. Each species has its own particular song and the female will respond only to males of her species. Some mole crickets even go so far as to modify the entrance to their burrows to amplify their songs. Cicadas (Order Hemiptera) are also well known for their chirping but they produce the sounds in a quite different way from the Orthoptera. A pair of ridged drums or 'tymbals' at the base of the abdomen are moved to produce sounds in the same way as a rounded tin lid pressed in by a finger. The cicada's song serves to assemble the local population of males and females of the same species into a small group.

Praying mantid *(Eremiaphila* sp.*)*. Exceptionally well camouflaged for the stony ground on which they occur, these mantids are rarely noticed. Mantids overwinter as eggs deposited in cases on twigs or grass stems and so appear in abundance in spring (WAS)

Damsel-fly *(Pseudagrion* sp.*)*. The resting position shown here is typical of the Family Coenagrionidae. These damsel - flies are poor fliers but will take flying as well as stationary prey (EJG)

The rains that herald the future appearance of the grasshoppers also signal that of the caterpillars, the cicadas and other Hemiptera such as the plant-sucking shield bugs and, last but not least, the mantids. The mantids are a suborder of the Dictyoptera, the remainder of the group being composed of cockroaches. The praying mantids are all characterised by the peculiar form of the front legs. They have a row of sharp spines along the opposed margins of the second and third sections of the leg. Sitting motionless as if in an attitude of prayer, with these powerful raptorial legs raised together the mantid awaits its prey. A twentieth of a second is all that is required for these legs to shoot out and impale an unsuspecting insect between the rows of spines. There are at least two mantids in Kuwait one of which is green or brown with white speckling and another which is sandy brown. Under normal circumstances both are extremely well camouflaged, the former inhabiting bushes and the latter the stony desert surface.

Dragonfly *(Selysiothemis nigra)*. The shape of the wings and the pattern of veins on them are the major features used to distinguish between the different groups of the Odonata. This species belongs to the Family Libellulidae (KJM)

The previous mention of migratory insects did not exhaust the list of those insects that migrate and the Odonata (dragonflies) is one order that should be included. These long-bodied, keen-sighted, flying predators have aquatic larvae and need relatively still waters in which to breed. This limits the number that breed in Kuwait and many of those that are seen will be migrants from more northerly areas. The 5000 or so species of dragon-fly can be divided into two major subgroups. Heavily built 'dragonflies' hold their wings extended laterally when at rest, whilst the slender 'damsel-flies' fold them together along the back. Dragonflies capture prey on the wing and flying insects are caught in a cage formed by the out-spread legs before being carried to the mouth.

Adult ant-lions resemble damsel-flies but in fact belong to the Order Neuroptera which also includes alder-flies and lacewings. The larvae of the ant-lion are probably better known and these insects, which are characteristic of the summer, are often known as 'demons of the dust'. Their cone-shaped pits can be seen dotted about in the sand

Dragonfly *(Lindenia tetraphyla)*. An adept aerial predator, the dragonfly's air speed may be as much as 40-50 k.p.h. The collision impact with its prey is absorbed by the dragonfly's thorax without throwing it off balance (ANHG)

Ant - lion larva (Myrmeleontidae). All that is normally seen of this larva is the open jaws at the bottom of its conical pit in hard sand. Prey falling into the pit are encouraged in their descent by sand flicked up at them by the larva (LC)

Praying mantid *(Blepharopsis medica)*. The lively colouration of this insect may serve as camouflage or as a lure. The mantid hunts by day, relying heavily on vision and a highly mobile head. Its diet is extremely varied and may even include small reptiles (AC)

and at the bottom of each pit lies a half buried ant-lion larva with vicious jaws wide open. The ant-lion is extremely hardy and can remain active at temperatures up to 48° C. It is also well able to withstand starvation and sometimes may go for several months without eating. Once prey has entered the trap, however, the ant-lion helps to seal its doom by accurately flicking sand to dislodge and tumble the hapless insect down into the waiting jaws.

The true flies or Diptera have only one pair of wings and are all too plentiful in the desert. If a man goes out into the desert without adequate clothing he may well, much to his repugnance, become covered in a seething mass of black flies. Typhoid, cholera, dysentry and malaria are but a few of the diseases transmitted by flies. The notoriety of these blood-sucking or scavenging flies, however, tends to overshadow the beneficial effects of the vast majority, which effectively control overall insect populations. Apart from the Hymenoptera, which are mentioned later, the Diptera contains the largest number of predatory and parasitic insects. These scavengers further help to maintain the balance of nature by converting decaying plant and animal material into simple substances that enter the ground and can be recycled by the plants.

The most common scavengers in the desert are the metallically coloured blowflies, for example *Calliphora erythrocephala* and *Lucilia sericata,* and the flesh flies (e.g. *Sarcophaga carnaria),* which lay their eggs on dead animals. This marks the first of several definite successive stages in the decay of a cadaver. Each stage has its characteristic insects and the later dry decay stages are dominated by

Hoverfly *(Syrphus corollae).* A good example of mimicry, the harmless hoverfly exhibits the warning colouration of bees and wasps (WAS)

the beetles, first the carrion beetles, then the skin beetles or dermestids such as *Dermestes crutpinus* and finally the dung beetles. The larvae of the hoverfly *Eristalis taeniops* also live in decaying organic matter whilst those of another hoverfly, *Syrphus corollae,* are parasitic on aphids and other Homoptera. Similarity of life cycles is clearly not assured by being members of the same family. As adults, hoverflies are usually brightly coloured black and yellow giving them a superficial resemblance to wasps; others are densely hairy and mimic bumblebees. Both are examples of the mimicry mentioned earlier, in which harmless animals gain protection from predators by mimicking dangerous or unpleasant ones. The adults are attracted to flowers and, as their English name indicates, are frequently observed poised in the air on rapidly beating wings.

The wasps and ants are the most conspicuous of the desert Hymenoptera, and the solitary wasps of the Families Sphecidae and Vespidae are pre-

Opposite: **Potter wasp** *(Delta campaniforme)*. Instead of excavating a burrow for its larvae, the potter wasp constructs nests of mud attached to trees or rock faces (KJM)

Thread-waisted wasp *(Podalonia* sp.*)*. Members of this genus have a preference for hairless nocturnal-feeding caterpillars of the moth Family Noctuidae. Although buried in the ground by day the caterpillar is located and excavated by the wasp to provision its own larvae (WAS)

Thread-waisted wasp *(Prionyx stchurowskii hyalinipennis)*. Whilst the larva of many wasps feed on animals, the adults are often nectar-feeders. This species provisions its larvae with grasshoppers (IW)

Opposite: **Parasitic wasp** *(Campsonieriella thoracica)*. This wasp of the Family Scoliidae is seen here in search of a host for its larvae. Once stung, a paralysed grub is buried deeper in the ground in a cell built by the wasp (KJM)

Ants (Formicidae). A small group of ants co-operate to carry a paralysed caterpillar away from the nest of a potter wasp (KJM)

dacious and provision their nests with a variety of insect larvae. Each species of wasp, however, specialises in a particular prey. The potter wasp *Vespa orientalis* specialises in caterpillars whereas the digger wasp *Philanthus triangulum* burrows into the ground and stores bees. After stinging the bee to death it is said to eat the honey before burial. Quite often the solitary wasps' stings only paralyse and do not kill their prey so that they remain fresh whilst the wasps' larvae are developing. The cuckoo wasp *Stizus succineus* lets certain thread-waisted wasps catch grasshoppers and then lays its own eggs on the victim. Spiders are the prey of the spider-wasp *Pompilius quadripunctatus,* which belongs to the family Pompilidae. It would be interesting to know whether this Kuwait wasp prepares its own burrow or uses that of its victim since members of this family practise both alternatives. The Lycosidae or wolf spiders are the principal victims and, surprising as it may seem, are reported to be totally panic-stricken at the sight of the wasp and do little in their own defence.

Ants are very common in desert regions and are probably the most successful of all insect groups.

In large part this success must be due to their extreme degree of sociality coupled with their caste system for the division of labour. The majority of the desert ants live in subterranean nests with little or no outwardly visible signs of their presence. The small, light yellowish Pharaoh Ant *(Monomorium pharaonis)* found in Kuwait lives mainly on seeds, especially of grasses, although it has now become a pest of many households. Harvester ants in general collect grass seeds and store them in granaries deep underground against times of famine. The store is well tended and any damp seeds are brought to the surface to be dried in the sun. The removal of germinating seeds from the granary has led to the erroneous idea that the ants actually plant seeds to ensure a future supply. As an alternative way of dealing with the relative scarcity of food in the desert, some ants have become speedy hunters of other insects. Species of *Cataglyphis,* including *C. maculatus* and *C. bicolor* found in Kuwait, are hunting ants. As a rule hunting workers act singly

Dung beetle *(Scarabaeus sacer).* Intent on rolling its food ball to its burrow, the persistent beetle is deterred by no obstacle. Once inside the burrow the beetle seals itself in until it has consumed the ball of faeces (WAS)

Termites (Hodotermitidae). These termites are to be seen during the day sheltering beneath stones or gnawing plant material under the cover of earth shields constructed at night. Some species found in the desert are known as harvester termites because they have the habit of storing bits of grass in their nests (MS)

so that the prey is no bigger than one ant can overpower and carry by itself. In some ants, however, the workers co-operate to overpower much larger prey and to drag it back to the nest before dismemberment and distribution to the colony.

It seems surprising that the desert worker ants can leave their nests, forage at random and then find their way back home over the featureless desert sands even when strong winds make odour trails impracticable. The answer lies in the ants' ability to orientate by using the sun. In some mysterious way the ants calculate the angle subtended by the sun and the nest and hold it constant on their return journey. Anyone can check this for himself by a simple experiment with a mirror. First find an ant returning home with some food, shade it from the sun on one side, and, with the mirror, present the sun's image on the other. The ant will immediately turn back and head off in the opposite direction, confident that that is where home is. For nocturnally foraging ants a similar moon-compass response serves equally well. Ants remove soil from their nests for nearly half the year and have a tremendous effect on soil structure and composition. Together with the white ants or termites, these insects have been described as doing the work of the earthworm from more temperate climates. The termites (Order Isoptera) are much more primitive insects than the ants and apart from their sociality bear little resemblance to true ants. In some ways it is a shame that there are no monolithic mound-building termites in Kuwait for these construct the most spectaclar and fascinating of the termite nests. The majority are instead subterranean nest-builders. Termites avoid all possible contact with light and free air, preferring to remain in their dark humid nests. Some even build mud and saliva 'concrete' surface tunnels to avoid the heat and light.

If there were a desert beetle as ferocious as the scorpion and camel spider there would indeed be a serious rival for the position as the symbol of the desert invertebrates, for without doubt the beetles or Coleoptera are the insects best adapted to desert life. Despite their imposing size and shape the life style of the Scarabaeidae preclude them from attaining fame as our imaginary champion. These are the dung beetles, the desert scavengers, which are seen diligently breaking up and burying the droppings of goats, camels and other animals. The best known exponent is the Sacred Beetle of Egypt *(Scarabaeus sacer)*, which is also found in Kuwait. Dung is collected and formed into a ball by being turned between the long slender back legs. Once finished the ball is trundled away by the beetle which walks backwards on its front legs. Its journey is often fraught with difficulties not the least of which is the danger of the ball rolling away from the beetle on steep inclines. The destination is a subterranean chamber where the animal seals itself away until it has consumed the ball. In the autumn a larger chamber is pro-visioned with several balls to provide for the developing egg. Occasionally two beetles will be seen rolling a ball together and this behaviour can be explained in one of two ways. In some species of dung beetles the male and female co-operate to build and provision a large breeding chamber, which may house several larvae. Alternatively it may be a case of one beetle having designs on another beetle's property and the true status of the partner reveals itself when the first beetle looses the ball momentarily. The second beetle trundles the ball off on its own leaving the first one search-ing for its meal!

Blister beetles (Meloidae) are also common in deserts and have vivid black and red, green, brown or blue warning colouration. When disturbed they

Opposite: **Blister beetle** *(Mylabris* sp.*)*. The aposematic or warning colouration helps predators to learn to avoid these beetles, which protect themselves by reflex bleeding. When disturbed they exude distasteful, and in some species poisonous, oily blood from their joints (KJM)

Ground beetle *(Graphipterus minutus)*. Shiny and somewhat flattened, this beetle is clearly identified by its distinctive black and white patterning (KJM)

Darkling beetle *(Blaps* sp.*)*. One of the larger aposematically black beetles found in Kuwait. If attacked by a predator a brown poisonous fluid is exuded from the beetle's body (ANHG)

secrete an oily substance from the joints of the legs containing cantharidin, which produces painful blisters on the skin. In the past this chemical has been widely used in the preparation of medicines, poisons and love potions. The larvae of these beetles are parasitic on the eggs of grasshoppers or bees. Those that parasitise bees climb onto a flower and hitch a lift back to the bee's nest on the unknowing host.

In the tiger beetles (Cicindelidae) both the larvae and the adults are predacious, feeding on a wide variety of small insects. The adult actively pursues its victims whilst the open-jawed larva props itself at the entrance to its burrow waiting for passing prey. *Cicindela nemoralis* is one species of tiger beetle found in Kuwait.

Calosoma imbricatum is a local representative of the ground beetles (Carabidae). Generally these beetles are bigger than tiger beetles and prey on caterpillars. As with many desert species of ground beetle *C. imbricatum* does not have wings. These nocturnal beetles are rarely seen, spending their days under rocks, in cracks and down the holes of scorpions and gerbils. They can survive long periods without eating; a close relative of *Blaps wiedemanni*, another local beetle, is recorded as having been kept for five years without feeding.

The ladybirds (Coccinellidae) are a well-known group of brightly coloured beetles. The larvae and

Opposite: **Ground beetle** *(Thermophilum duodecimguttatum)*. This fast moving predatory beetle is responsible for many of the headless black beetles seen in the desert (IW)

Darkling beetle *(Erodius octocostatus)*. A beetle of winter and spring which, when not feeding, buries itself in loose slip-face sand as is common in gullies of the Jal Az-Zor (DAC)

Darkling beetle *(Adesmia cancellata)*. Several of Kuwait's Tenebrionidae are black and similar in shape, but can be distinguished largely by the fused wing covers (IW)

adults are both predacious on aphids. The Eleven-spot Ladybird *(Coccinella undecimpunctata)* is common in the Middle East and, as a migratory species, its appearance can be quite sudden and dramatic reaching epidemic proportions on occasion. In 1939 an estimated 4,500 million were washed ashore along a 22 km stretch of the north coast of Egypt west of Alexandria, but millions more survived to continue the migration. The migration is a journey to and from localities where they mass together to hibernate in a dormant state similar in principle to the diapause state of the molluscs mentioned earlier.

The last group to be considered are the most well adapted insects to desert life. The darkling beetles (Tenebrionidae) will be familiar to all through two ubiquitous representatives. Both the small tribolium flour beetle and the much larger tenebrio beetles are found in all stages in meal, flour and stored goods. The tenebrio beetle larvae are often known as meal-worms. One aspect of the darkling beetles' success in deserts is their ability to live on dry food without any water and their extreme waterproofing. If *Tenebrio molitor* is kept in air with a relative humidity of 95 % the beetle literally blows up. The metabolic water produced as a by-product of the normal body processes cannot escape. These beetles are omnivorous, feeding on vegetable matter, carrion and dung but can and do survive long periods without eating.

Opposite: **Seven-spot ladybird** *(Coccinella septempunctata)*. The spots are variable in size and shape. The wing cases after hibernation are more yellow and lighter in colour than those of the summer generation of adults (KJM)

Darkling beetle *(Paraplatyope arabica)*. Despite their name, not all darkling beetles are black. In temperate regions stones and rubbish commonly provide shelter for ground beetles but in arid regions their ecological niche is filled by darkling beetles (DAC)

Darkling beetle *(Pimelia arabica)*. Having excavated a small hole, this female is about to desposit her egg case in it (WAS)

Opposite: **Darkling beetle** *(Pimelia arabica)*. When running from possible danger this beetle seems almost to be standing on its head (IW)

Darkling beetle *(Ocnera* sp.*)*. An aggregation rather than a social group, the beetles have been attracted to the same place by preference for a particular microclimate (WAS)

Adesmia cancellata, Adesmia aenescens and *Adesmia cothurnata* are all members of the same genus found in Kuwait and all are typical Tenebrionidae. They do not have wings and the wingcases are fused to form a cavity about the body. This air space insulates the beast and helps reduce further water loss by evaporation. The breathing holes or 'spiracles' of the tracheal system open into it. All these beetles are black, as are two other local species, *Ocnera philistina* and *Ocnera hispida,* and many suggestions have been made to explain why most desert species are this colour. The explanations range from a heat-absorbing device to an ultraviolet ray shield, but it is more probably another example of aposematic or warning colouration, since they appear to have an unpleasant taste as well as smell and are avoided by predators. Because all the species are black a predator has only to taste one individual of one species for all individuals of all the species to gain protection.

In talking about predation this chapter ends as it began. It is not enough that animals simply adapt themselves to the harsh physical conditions of a desert, they must also show the ability to adapt to other aspects of the situation. The invertebrates, particularly the arachnids and the beetles, are well adapted for desert living simply because of their solution to the general problems posed by living on land instead of in water. Other pressures posed by biological rather than physical needs, and which include finding food and avoiding being eaten, are also extremely important and influence the animals' body functions, shape and behaviour.

Reptiles

By
Bill Stuart and David Clayton

To people living in Kuwait reptiles are commonplace. Lizards of various kinds are frequently seen scurrying across the desert; geckos share human habitation; snakes are shy but command respect when seen; and turtles and sea snakes are caught in trawl nets by the Gulf fishermen.

Unlike birds or mammals, reptiles are cold-blooded animals and rely principally on the environment to provide heat to maintain their body temperature. The characteristic dependence on temperature is the most important physical factor governing the lives and habits of the land reptiles,

Dhub *(Uromastyx microlepis)*. During the summer the bright yellow colour reflects the light and helps to keep the animal cool (CWTP)

including those found in Kuwait. A great proportion of the daily activity of these animals is devoted to responding to the environmental temperature. Basking, perching, changing body posture, shade-seeking, shuttling and burrowing are the commonest responses. In most cases, such behaviour is so effective that the reptile's temperature is maintained within fairly narrow limits and fluctuates much less than that of its surroundings. Besides such efficient behavioural adaptations, the anatomy and certain body functions of reptiles have evolved in such a way as to enable these animals to live in an arid environment. Water conservation is assisted by their thick skin, which is usually covered with horny scales. The skin has few glands and, in comparison with amphibians, birds and mammals, is relatively impermeable so that water lost through evaporation is reduced to a minimum. Water lost through excretion is reduced by two main adaptations. Firstly, salt is excreted as a very concentrated brine through nasal glands and secondly, the kidney is able to remove nitrogenous waste products in an insoluble form such as uric acid.

The land reptiles of Kuwait are representatives of the Order Squamata, which represents the flowering of modern reptiles, both in number and kind. Whilst the snakes, because of their diet and manner of locomotion, are relatively uniform, the lizards show a considerable range of body form, reflecting adaptation to different life styles.

Agamids or rainbow lizards are widely distributed about the deserts of the Old World and they are mostly flattish terrestrial forms. The majority of these are insectivorous, although the most well known member of this group in Kuwait - the Dhub *(Uromastyx microlepis)* - is essentially herbivorous. This large reptile is widespread here and is easily recognised by its tortoise-like head and short thick tail covered with whorls of large spiny scales. It is commonly seen basking in the sun at the raised entrance to its deep spiralling burrow. This lizard provides one of the more spectacular examples of temperature regulation by pigment changes in the skin. According to its heat requirements the animal can rapidly change colour from a dark slate-grey to a bright sulphur yellow. The light colour reflects the heat whereas the dark hue absorbs it and so warms the creature. Dark phase individuals are typical of winter conditions although in the summer, as it emerges from its

Blue-throated Agamid *(Agama blandfordi)*. This is an unusual perching place for this lizard, which normally prefers bushes (CWTP)

Dhub *(Uromastyx microlepis)*. Looking like some prehistoric monster the Dhub surveys its surroundings. Still in its dark phase this animal is absorbing heat until its body reaches an optimum temperature (DAC)

Pallid Agamid *(Agama pallida)*. Bold patterning provides the animal with good camouflage on stony ground (WAS)

burrow at daybreak, the Dhub may be dark, becoming lighter as it gets warmer. The stance of the Dhub during this early morning basking phase is typical of many agamids. It stands motionless in the sun with its body raised off the ground to avoid loss of heat to the sand. In some cases the animal can be seen leaning on an Arfaj *(Rhanterium epapposum)* bush with only its hind feet on the ground, thereby maximising absorption of the sun's heat and minimising conductive losses.

The Dhub is considered a delicacy by the nomadic Bedouin, but catching the animal can be difficult. It is slow when cold and so does not stray far from the safety of its burrow but, once its body temperature has risen to the levels required for normal activity, it can move very fast. The spiny tail, which can be swung with painful results for the victim, is this creature's main defensive weapon. If the lizard is cornered away from its burrow, the would-be captor is deterred by the mace-like tail and by the frightening threat display. The Dhub blows itself up and then exhales with a wide-open mouth, emitting a loud hiss. It takes a lot of concentration to remember that this is a harmless

111

herbivore! A similar and equally alarming threat display is exhibited by the carnivorous Desert Monitor *(Varanus griseus)* described later.

The Blue-throated Agamid *(Agama blandfordi)* is a rather charming lizard most frequently seen perching at the top of a medium-sized shrub, although other perch sites may be chosen. This behaviour also has a thermoregulatory function. During the day the temperature is highest at soil level and gradually decreases with increasing height above the ground. Consequently, reptiles can influence their body temperature by perching at different heights. Further regulation is achieved by perching in the open or in the shade of these shrubs. The Blue-throated Agamid takes its name from the colour of its gular pouch, which is used as a signal in courtship and threat displays with other members of the same species. When rivals meet, both bob up and down repeatedly, raising and lowering the front half of the body. If they are the same size the lizards threaten one another with open jaws and lash with their strong tails. Many males have shortened or broken tails as a result of such fights. Normally the lizard is greyish with a white underbelly but during the display or fighting it rapidly changes colour, with the victor becoming bright blue. If approached by Man, the agamid's gular flap is erected and turns blue in the typical threat display. However, closer approach will frighten the lizard and the colour quickly fades.

Bosc's Sand Lizard *(Acanthodactylus boskianus)*. The body is well clear of the ground to avoid contact with the hot sand (WAS)

Short-nosed Desert Lizard. *(Eremias brevirostris = Mesalina brevirostris)*. A well camouflaged animal, it is alert to the first sign of danger (WAS)

To complete the agamids of Kuwait, there are: the Pallid Agamid *(Agama pallida),* a lizard found in the stony desert areas, and the Toad-headed Agamid *(Phrynocephalus maculatus)* which prefers sandier areas. The Pallid Agamid relies on camouflage for defence and is sandy or rusty-brown in colour. It has two or three broad dark bands across the flattened abdomen, which help break up the animal's outline when it remains stationary among the stones. The Toad-headed Agamid is similar in appearance but instead of having a barred tail the distal third is entirely black. This lizard can bury itself in the sand in less than five seconds and, although this may be a useful way of avoiding danger, it is more probably a method of temperature regulation.

The true lizards, Lacertidae, are widely distributed over Asia and Africa and are extremely common. They tend to be diurnal in habit and consequently are probably the most frequently seen desert lizards. Members of this group exhibit two kinds of adaptation to their environment according to whether they are 'sand-runners' or 'sand-swimmers'. Most of the lacertids of Kuwait are sand-runners, having the toes of the fore and hind limbs fringed with elongated scales. This gives the animals greater mobility on the sand by increasing the surface in contact, in the same manner as snow shoes on loose snow.

Lacertids move extremely rapidly and the tail may be held well above the body as a counterpoise. The Short-nosed Desert Lizard *(Eremias brevirostris =*

Lacertid lizard *(Acanthodactylus scutellatus).* Basking in the sun, the lizard exposes its broad, flattened body to the full force of the sun (WAS)

Fringe-toed Sand Lizard *(Acanthodactylus schmidti).* Low bushes provide shelter, protection and good hunting grounds for many lizards (WAS)

Lacertid Lizard *(Acanthodactylus scutellatus)*. The enlarged scales on the toes of sand-running lizards help in movement across loose sand (CWTP)

Opposite: **Lacertid lizard** *(Acanthodactylus scutellatus)*. The pineal or 'third eye' can be seen clearly on the top of the head behind the eyes. The pineal is light sensitive and is the receptor that controls temperature regulation (CWTP)

Lacertid lizard *(Acanthodactylus ophoedurus)*. This lizard is easily identified by its patterning and by the absence of a pronounced neck (VRK)

Stone Gecko *(Bunopus tuberculatus)*. This is one of the commonest and most widespread geckos and is found in all areas of Kuwait (WAS)

Mesalina brevirostris), whose tail is twice as long its body, is commonly seen moving in this fashion. It is, however, the only Kuwait lacertid without fringed toes. To the inexperienced eye, the sand-runners are difficult to distinguish from each other. Bosc's Sand Lizard *(Acanthodactylus boskianus)* is a small slender lizard with a long tail, sandy colouring and three dark bands along its back. *Acanthodactylus schmidti* or the Fringe-toed Sand Lizard is also sandy-coloured but is slightly larger and has darker evenly spaced spots on its back. *Acanthodactylus scutellatus* resembles these two but can be recognised by its distinctive brown and blue net-like pattern. The fourth *Acanthodactylus (A. opheodurus)* is easier to recognise, having a head narrower than its body and a neck that is not pronounced. It has a dark head and body with longitudinal lines of tan markings interspersed with fine cream streaks. The lacertids all live in burrows usually excavated in the sand under bushes where there is ample shade. Body temperatures are

Keeled Rock Gecko *(Cyrtodactylus scaber)*. The regenerated tail and the hooked toes for climbing are clearly shown in this lizard (WAS)

maintained by shuttling repeatedly between sunlight and shade.

In many ways the Gekkonidae or geckos are the most unusual and endearing reptiles found in Kuwait. They are characterised by their large eyes, which have a vertical or odd-shaped pupil, and by the absence of eyelids. Most are insectivorous and nocturnal and, although the local species are unusually quiet, the geckos are the only lizards capable of making definite noises. These range from feeble croaks and chirps to loud barks. Geckos have a rather delicate skin with small granular scales and the tails of many are dispensible (but regenerable) in the interests of self-preservation. The Stone Gecko *(Bunopus tuberculatus)* is probably the commonest and most widespread one in Kuwait and can sometimes be found in the daytime by turning over stones or pieces of rubbish. It is grey-brown on top with brown transverse bars, but can easily be recognised by the broad dark line running backwards from the nostrils to meet behind the head. The Keeled Rock Gecko *(Cyrtodactylus scaber)* resembles the Stone Gecko in general shape but is a transparent pink with scattered brown marks on its back. It is found in rocky areas and near houses. *Stenodactylus doriae* and *Stenodactylus sleveni* are two geckos having plump pinkish bodies, covered in fine dark and large tan markings, and short barred tails. They are both found in regions of gravel and loose sand. These two species are difficult to tell apart but the toes, especially of the fore-feet, of *S. doriae* are flattened with strong fringes typical of sand-runners.

The Yellow-bellied House Gecko *(Hemidactylus flaviviridis)* is the largest member of the family found in Kuwait and is probably the one that springs to mind when geckos are mentioned. It can climb well, even on glass, and is sometimes seen hunting insects near wall-lights that attract night-flying insects. To do so it relies on flattened adhesive pads located on all the digits of its feet. These pads consist of rows of lamellae, each of which is covered in hundreds of thousands of fine setae or hairs. All setae bear between a hundred and a thousand branches, each ending in a small suction cup. The climbing ability of some geckos, however, can be attributed to sharp recurving claws as in the Keeled Rock Gecko and *Hemidactylus persica,* the Persian Gecko, which is also found in Kuwait. The Yellow-bellied House Gecko is somewhat unusual in having both pads and claws to assist in climbing.

The occasional discovery of a small clutch of gecko eggs in some dark corner of the house, perhaps behind a bottle that has not been moved for some time, serves to remind one that reptiles lay eggs. Internal fertilisation and the evolution of the cleidoic egg (or closed-box egg) were the main factors enabling reptiles to become the first fully terrestrial vertebrates insofar as they had no need to return to water to breed.

Gecko *(Stenodactylus slevini).* Normally nocturnal, this animal will simply freeze if discovered during the day, relying on its cryptic colouration for concealment (DAC)

The Scincidae (skinks) is a large family with a great diversity of types in other parts of the world, but in Kuwait there are only three representatives. These are the sand-swimmers of Kuwait and all exhibit profound modifications for rapid burrowing in loose sand. The largest skink *(Scincus scincus)* is found in coastal dune areas and is ideally designed for its life just below the surface of the loose sand. Yellow in colour, it has a shovel-like snout and a long tapering body. The smooth scales and reduced limbs do not impede the skink as it glides through the sand. Sand is prevented from entering the nasal passages by valve-like closures and the mouth is protected when closed by having the lower jaw resting in the upper. Normal breathing by rib cage expansion and contraction would be a problem to the skink when buried because loose sand would tend to cave in on it during exhalation. The problem is solved by the expedient of using movement of the underbelly to ventilate the lungs. The belly, protected from falling sand, is flat during inhalation and concave during exhalation. This method of breathing is also used by the animal on the surface and the apparent total immobility leads the observer to believe it dead. Closer examination galvanises the skink into action and the creature dives head first into the sand as if it were water. *Scincus mitranus* is very similar in form and habits but is distinguished from *S. scincus* by its sandy colour with denser markings and the absence of visible auditory openings. A third skink, *Ablepharus pannonicus* is found in the northern border regions.

Another burrowing reptile is the Arabian Worm Lizard *(Diplometopon zarudnyi)*, a small pink or purplish, legless lizard. It is a member of the Family Amphisbaenidae, the name deriving from the Greek for 'going both ways'. Ancient authors thought it had two heads and that one woke up when it was time for it to take over guarding the eggs. This mistaken idea arose because the animal has minute eyes covered by transparent scales and when disturbed it waves its tail in the same way as a snake waves its head. The body is covered in ring-like scales giving it the appearance of a long earthworm. The similarity does not end here for the lizard creeps forwards (or backwards) using a motion similar to that of the worm. Alternatively it can move by throwing its body into vertical undulations. It feeds on small invertebrates and has large pointed teeth for piercing their hard cuticle. When handled it will sometimes bite and

Yellow-bellied House Gecko *(Hemidactylus flaviviridis)*. This is the largest of the geckos found in Kuwait. Claws and pads on the broadened toes assist the animal to climb (WAS)

Skink *(Ablepharus pannonicus)*. The northern reaches of Kuwait probably represent the southern-most extent of this animal's range (WAS)

Skink *(Scincus scincus)*. The broad shovel-like head, smooth body and shortened limbs are all adaptations to burrowing (DAC)

Arabian Worm Lizard. *(Diplometopon zarudnyi).* This legless lizard resembles an earthworm and spends most of its life underground (CWTP)

by rotating its head will painfully remove a small core of flesh.

The last, but by no means the least, of the lizards found in Kuwait is the Desert Monitor or Wirral *(Varanus griseus).* It is a member of the Family Varanidae or monitor group which contains the largest living lizard, the Komodo Dragon of Java. The local monitor is not nearly as spectacular as the legendary Dragon but is still the largest of Kuwait's lizards, reaching some 140 cm in length. It has a long head and neck and the slender body is supported by strong legs equipped with vicious-looking claws. The long tapering tail can be used as a whip to attack a rival but, unlike that of many other reptiles, it cannot be shed. Some features of the Wirral, such as its long forked tongue and its propensity for swallowing prey whole, are more commonly associated with snakes. It is carnivorous and will eat a wide variety of animals as well as carrion. Consequently, wounds inflicted by the animal's bite often turn septic and, if only because of this, the animal's threat display should be treated with more respect than that of a Dhub.

As we have seen, temperature control is a major concern for the lizards of arid lands and clearly the same considerations will apply to snakes found in such regions. Their highly specialised, limbless,

Desert Monitor *(Varanus griseus).* The large powerful jaws serve to emphasize the threat display of this large carnivorous reptile (CWTP)

serpentine form adds yet another problem. In comparison with a lizard of the same weight or volume a snake has a much greater surface area and consequently will heat and cool more quickly than the lizard. This is one reason for the apparent absence of snakes in the desert; if the snake remains in the open its temperature, relative to that of the lizard, will increase faster. Snakes are more often found at night or under stones, wood, bushes and in burrows where the micro-climate is subject to less variation.

The most primitive of the Kuwait snakes is the Flowerpot Blind Snake *(Typhlops braminus)*, so called because it has extended its distribution by being carried in the pots of cultivated plants. It avoids the environmental rigours by spending its life underground. Not surprisingly for a subterranean animal, the eyes are vestigial and able to discern only differences in light intensity. It has a smooth white or pink skin covered with small brown and pink scales. In Kuwait, it is found in soil rich in humus and probably feeds on worms and insects. Having only a small mouth and no teeth in the lower jaw it is quite harmless to Man.

Wirral *(Varanus griseus)*. Lashing with its whip-like tail, hissing and increasing its body size by sucking in air all succeed in making the defensive threat display of the Wirral very intimidating (WAS)

Sand Boa *(Eryx jayakari)*. The only boa constrictor in Kuwait, it is rarely seen, emerging from the sand only to catch its prey (CWTP)

Opposite: **Sand Boa** *(Eryx jayakari)*. Having found the head of the lizard the boa begins the process of aligning it so that the lizard can be swallowed whole. Intervals between successive meals for the boa, as for other snakes, are often irregular (DAC)

Sand Boa *(Eryx jayakari)*. Constrained by the boa's body coils the *Acanthodactylus* lizard was initially prevented from escaping by being grasped in the boa's mouth (DAC).

A second subterranean snake, the Sand Boa *(Eryx jayakari)*, is the only Kuwait representative of the family Boidae (pythons and boa constrictors) and can be recognised by the vestigial hindlimbs that occur as spurs on either side of the cloacal opening. The Sand Boa grows to 50 cm and has a very glossy golden-brown skin with transverse white bars. Underneath it is white. The burrowing adaptations of this snake are reminiscent of those of the skinks. The head is wedge-shaped, the nostrils valved, the jaw countersunk and the scales smooth. Although it is rarely seen, the Sand Boa is probably fairly common in soft sandy areas. Like other boas it kills its prey by constriction.

Two-thirds of the world's snakes are members of the Colubridae, so it is no surprise that four of the snakes in Kuwait are from this group. Two are venomous. The strikingly marked Leaf-nosed Snake *(Lytorhynchus diadema)* is fairly common and derives its name from the large shield on its nose. It is found in regions of sand or bush and when disturbed often forms two coils with the head in the striking position. Even a young specimen will hiss loudly and attempt repeated strikes, but despite this display the snake is not poisonous. A second species, *Lytorhynchus gaddi* may also be found in Kuwait. The other non-venomous colubrid is the Rat Snake *(Coluber ventromaculatus)*, which is found all over Arabia and lives in rocky regions and in old buildings. It strikes at and eats small mammals, birds and lizards and has

Sand Boa *(Eryx jayakari)*. Occasionally readjusting the coils, the boa may take as much as an hour to subdue its prey. During this period the first exploratory movements to locate the lizard's head are made (DAC)

Leaf-nosed Snake *(Lytorhynchus diadema)*. This harmless snake adopts this posture when disturbed. It also hisses loudly and makes mock strikes (WAS)

small but strong sharp teeth. The Arabian Rear-fanged Snake *(Malpolon moilensis)* is possibly the most commonly seen snake. At the rear of the mouth it has poison glands with which it paralyses its prey during feeding. As far as larger animals and Man are concerned the location of the fangs and the small gape of the mouth make it difficult for the snake to inject its venom. Nevertheless, as a venomous animal it should still be treated with respect. The snake can grow to well over a metre in length and has the ability to move with the front half of its body raised from the ground. It can also flatten the body immediately behind the head giving it a cobra-like hooded appearance and fostering the idea of there being a cobra in Kuwait. This 'hood' is used during threat displays

Hissing Sand Snake *(Psammophis schokari)*. This snake can move very rapidly but when resting adopts the typical posture shown here (WAS)

but also has a possible secondary function as a thermoregulatory device. By increasing the surface area exposed to the sun the animal could heat up more quickly than would otherwise be possible. Certainly, there are many snakes that show such postural changes as a means of regulating temperature. Flattening is sometimes accompanied by tilting the whole body on one edge so that the flattened area is at right angles to the sun and there is less contact with the cool ground. When snakes begin to cool in the evening, they form a compact coil thereby reducing the effective surface area through which heat is lost. Whether the snakes of Kuwait use these particular mechanisms is still a matter for future careful observation and study. The Arabian Rear-fanged Snake can easily be recognised by the hood or more reliably by its prominent eyes and the large dark kidney-shaped mark behind them. The body is a pale sandy-brown or grey with a pattern of black dots joined by thin lines resembling an open weave. The underside is yellow or white.

The Hissing Sand Snake *(Psammophis schokari)* is also rear-fanged and, although it is one of the smaller snakes, it is still to be treated with respect for little is known of the venom's toxicity. The snake is to be found in rocky regions and old houses and is sometimes seen (possibly basking) draped over a bush. It is a slim snake varying from golden-brown through olive to grey with buff streaks. A black line runs back from the nasal openings through the eye and onto the neck.

Snakes use several methods of moving about, the three most common being lateral undulation, concertina and rectilinear locomotion. In all cases

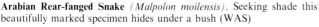

Arabian Rear-fanged Snake *(Malpolon moilensis)*. Seeking shade this beautifully marked specimen hides under a bush (WAS)

a fixed point in the form of an irregularity of the surface against which the animal can push is required. These methods become highly inefficient when the surface gives as the snake exerts pressure against it. Side-winding, the fourth method of locomotion, can be adopted in such circumstances. The Horned Viper *(Cerastes cerastes)*, the most venomous of the snakes so far discussed, has perfected this form of locomotion for moving over loose sand. Whilst defying verbal description, the body of a sidewinding snake is thrown into lateral loops and lies almost at right angles to the direction of movement. The head, however, is pointed in the right direction, and the snake appears to 'roll' along the ground leaving behind the characteristic hook-shaped track. The Horned Viper derives its name from the horn-like scales behind its eyes but some members of this species do not possess them and are then colloquially known as Sand Vipers. Both forms possess a stocky body, a short tapering tail and a broad arrow-shaped head. The eyes are large with vertical slit pupils and are set high on the sides of the head. The colour varies from sandy-grey to reddish-brown with darker bars across the back. The snake is sluggish and often lies buried in the sand or coiled up under a bush. It is therefore dangerous to walk in loose sand, where these snakes occur, without adequate footwear and some considerable care. Even if it is buried with only its eyes exposed the outlines of the coils on the surface, made as the snake sinks itself into the sand,

Rat Snake *(Coluber ventromaculatus)*. This long and slender snake is easily identified by the dark marking over the head between the eyes and which ends as a dark comma below each eye (DAC)

Horned Viper *(Cerastes cerastes)*. The powerful body of this dangerous reptile is coiled ready for striking (CWTP)

give its position away. The snake coils itself up and then, by moving its ribs alternately, it works the sand out from under and over the body. When disturbed, vipers will generally retreat and produce a distinctive warning display. They pass their coils along each other to produce a hissing noise. The mouth may also be opened showing a bright pink interior but this is no indication of the snake's readiness to strike. Do not be misled into thinking that the striking distance is only as far as the first loop of the body behind the head. Vipers can, and may, strike with their full body length. A full bite is not necessary for the injection of venom. The Viperidae have an efficient venom delivery apparatus involving large hollow fangs that can be erected and stabbed into the prey. The poison sacs contract at the moment of contact and inject the poison. Even young vipers are born with functional fangs. Removal of them does not render the snake permanently harmless as new fangs will replace them.

Black Desert Cobra *(Walterinnesia aegyptia)*. Although there is at least one other black snake in Arabia, a burrowing viper, it is almost certain that the 'yaim' of Bedouin folklore is this rare, jet black hoodless cobra. Cobra venom is generally neurotoxic and extremely dangerous to Man and these snakes should be left well alone (KR)

In contrast to those of the vipers, the poison fangs of another family of snakes, the Elapidae, are fixed but hidden by palatal folds in the upper jaw at about the level of the nasal openings. Since their venom is several times as potent as that of vipers, however, the Elapidae, are exceedingly dangerous. This family includes sea snakes, which are mentioned in the chapter on marine life, mambas, coral snakes and cobras.

The Arabian Rear-fanged Snake may be mistaken for a cobra, but the error is soon realised when faced by a real one. The Arabian Cobra *(Naja haje arabica)* can grow to over 2m and, having the ability to raise almost half its body in the air and flare its hood, it looks at least twice as big as the biggest snake you ever saw. Whilst this snake is relatively common in the Arabian Peninsula, none have been recorded in Kuwait. A second, much rarer one, the Black Desert Cobra (*Walterinnesia aegyptia*), however, was found recently for the first time. With fewer than a dozen ever having been recorded in Arabia, this lustrous deadly black beast is indeed a creature to inspire myths. Endowed by tradition with supernatural powers, this snake is feared by the Bedouin who believe that the spirit of a killed snake will exact retribution on the murderer.

Unlike other cobras, the Black Desert Cobra does not have a hood, but at over 120 cm in length, its jet black appearance and loud hissing must be a sufficient deterrent to all but the foolhardy. Apart from the fact that it is probably nocturnal little is known of the snake's life style and even less can be said about its nature. Where there is agreement that sea snakes are genuinely non-aggressive, for example, no such generalisation can be made of this cobra; some observers report that the animal is docile and others that it is extremely aggressive needing little provocation to attack. Whatever its true nature the beast is best left alone and certainly should not be killed. The Black Desert Cobra may well be one of the World's rare animals, and, the Bedouin may be right.

We shall now finally consider the Green Toad (*Bufo viridis*), which is not a reptile but is the only amphibian in Kuwait. The absence of more members of the Amphibia can undoubtedly be attributed to their naked skin and the need to breed in water. In Kuwait, the toad is seen in the north and at other places were there is standing water sufficient for the hatching and growth of the tadpoles before they metamorphose into the adult form. The animals are rarely seen during hibernation, which lasts from September until the late spring when they emerge to mate. The male is slightly smaller than the female and sings with a long trilling whistle that can be heard over great distances. Both sexes have a skin that is extremely warty and variable in colour. The back is pale grey or olive-green with darker green black-edged blotchy markings. In the shade the toad is darker but changes to pale grey with grass-green markings in less then ten minutes when exposed to the sun.

Green Toad *(Bufo viridis)*. The only amphibian to be found in Kuwait is represented here by a female of the species (WAS)

Birds

By
Bill Stuart and Charles Pilcher

Having the ability to fly, sometimes almost effortlessly, means that birds are able to travel over very long distances. Moreover, the seasonal availability of food obliges many species to journey from one part of the globe to another, a well known phenomenon referred to as migration; the result is that birds are widely distributed throughout the world. These factors are clearly important for Kuwait because inspection of the records of birds sighted here shows that the majority of

Turtle Doves *(Streptopelia turtur)*, L 27 cm. Large flocks of these doves pass through the Country in spring and autumn. The birds shown here have the paler plumage more typical of the desert form (CWTP)

species are migrants in passage, either travelling from winter quarters to their breeding-grounds in the spring or making the return journey in the autumn. In addition, the climate during the winter months is relatively mild in Kuwait and a number of species travel from northern latitudes at the onset of cold weather to spend the winter here. In fact, if the only birds to be seen in this country were those that are permanent residents, there would be merely a handful of species present.

It is becoming increasingly clear that Kuwait is on a cross-roads of two fairly important migration routes and these bring large numbers of birds through the country in both spring and autumn. The preceding, cooler, wet months ensure a good food supply in the spring and the variety and number of birds passing through the country are greater then than in autumn. This is a consequence of loop-migration, the phenomenon where a migratory species will fly along one route in spring but return along a different route in autumn. In winter more favourable conditions for birds prevail in Africa, Pakistan and India than in Europe and northern Asia and it is not surprising, therefore, to find that the two routes through Kuwait are generally in either an east-west or north-south direction. This does not, of course, explain entirely why birds choose to fly over Kuwait. It is well known that birds use a number of fairly well defined migration routes and these routes often avoid high mountain ranges or large stretches of open water. For example, many birds from Europe fly down the length of Italy, pass through Malta and enter Africa through Libya. Thousands of birds of prey even fly around the eastern end of

Nightjar *(Caprimulgus europaeus)*, L 27 cm. Unless flushed from their resting places on the ground or along a branch, nightjars are reluctant to fly during the day. Their large eyes and huge gape, enhanced by the scoop-net of bristles are adaptations to assist in catching night-flying insects on the wing. The Nightjar is a passage migrant (LC)

the Mediterranean Sea and cross from Europe to Asia over the Bosphorus. One of the migration routes that pass through Kuwait is from eastern Europe along the rivers of Turkey, Syria and Iraq eastwards to Pakistan and India. The second route is from central and southern Russia down the western side of the Zagros Mountains and on to southern Arabia or even into eastern, central and exceptionally southern Africa.

Two further factors can have marked effects on the number and variety of birds seen in Kuwait. Firstly, climatic conditions in this and distant regions are a significant influence. Unusually severe winter conditions in the north will force even hardy species to travel further south than they otherwise would. Also, a particularly dry winter season in the Arabian peninsula will increase the likelihood of migrants that have crossed that region stopping and resting in Kuwait, where fresh water is available all year round. The second factor is a phenomenon known as dispersal, which is the general tendency for animals to increase their distribution range. After one or more good breeding seasons the pressure on food sources and

Namaqua Dove *(Oena capensis)*, L 28 cm. Although very uncommon, the occurrence here of this attractive, small dove may be on the increase. Being the only long-tailed dove in this region it is easily identified (CWTP)

available habitats increases and encourages birds to range further afield. Dispersal may account for the increased sightings in Kuwait of the Namaqua Dove *(Oena capensis)*, a bird that is resident throughout much of Iran.

Thus, the birds of Kuwait are essentially those of the Western Palaeartic Zone, a zoogeographical region that extends from the mid-Atlantic Ocean in the west to the Caspian Sea in the east and from the Polar Cap in the north to the latitude of the central Sahara Desert in the south. Kuwait is in the south-east corner on the very edge of the region and this does mean, as is illustrated by the Namaqua Dove, that a small number of birds from adjacent zones are occasionally sighted here.

Over 280 species have been recorded for Kuwait and, as in other chapters, only a fraction of those that may be seen can be dealt with here. In keeping with the main theme of the book, this chapter aims to introduce and foster an interest in the birdlife that comprises such an important part of Kuwait's natural heritage.

Curlew *(Numenius arquata)*, L 53-59 cm. This large brown wader is readily identified by its long curved bill and striking white rump. Throughout the winter it is commonly seen on the seashore and by fresh water (WAS)

In Winter

The start of the year is one of the poorest times for birds in Kuwait. There are few migratory movements and only residents and winter visitors are likely to be seen. However, some of these are quite interesting and others occur quite unexpect-

Greater Flamingoes *(Phoenicopterus ruber)*, L 127 cm. This large wader is unmistakable with its pink plumage, red and black wings and large down-curved beak. Throughout the period autumn to spring large numbers can be seen around Kuwait Bay (CWTP)

Avocets *(Recurvirostra avosetta)*, L 43 cm. One of the most easily recognised waders, the Avocet is usually seen from autumn to spring on the seashore. Small groups will often be seen wading along the water's edge, moving their long upturned bills from side to side to feed in the disturbed silt. At a distance the black crown and nape immediately separate this wader from the white-headed Crab Plover *(Dromas ardeola)* (CWTP)

Crab Plovers *(Dromas ardeola)*, L 35 cm. Recorded as breeding on the sandy mudflats of northern Kuwait, the Crab Plover is one of the few resident species. The larger pied waders are Oystercatchers *(Haematopus ostralegus)*, L 43 cm (WAS)

Ruff *(Philomachus pugnax)*, L 23-29 cm. Usually the Ruff is seen in winter when the plumage is extremely variable, having almost any mixture of black, red-brown, buff and white. The colour of the bill may be red, yellow or blackish and the legs orange, yellow or green (CWTP)

edly. Coastal areas are the best places to see a number of winter visitors. The mudflats around Kuwait Bay are host to considerable numbers of Greater Flamingoes *(Phoenicopterus ruber)*, which arrive in the late autumn and stay until March. They feed mainly on small crustaceans, which they dredge with their down-turned bills. In the same area one will also see great numbers of Redshank *(Tringa totanus)*, Dunlin *(Calidris alpina)* and Curlew *(Numenius arquata)*, some of which may have travelled from as far as the Arctic Circle. A similar journey will have been made by the Bar-tailed Godwit *(Limosa lapponica)*, which, unlike the Black-tailed Godwit *(Limosa limosa)*, occasionally remains here all winter. At this time of year the Greater *(Charadrius leschenaultii)* and Lesser *(Charadrius mongolus)* Sandplovers and the Ringed Plover *(Charadrius hiaticula)* resemble each other quite closely but careful observation will enable them to be recognised amongst the many other waders on the mudflats. Avocets *(Recurvirostra avosetta)* can often be seen in small groups at the water's edge, with their upcurved bills moving from side to side through the water to catch their food. On a world-wide basis the Crab Plover *(Dromas ardeola)* is quite rare but might still breed on the remoter mudflats of Bubiyan Island. This bird is the sole representative of its family, the Dromadidae, and inhabits, in addition to the coasts of the Arabian Gulf, the coasts of north-east Africa, coastal lagoons of Egypt and islands in the northern parts of the Indian Ocean. In most years a few Spoonbills *(Platalea leucorodia)*, birds named after their long spatulate bills, can be seen on the mudflats of Kuwait Bay. This is another bird that feeds by sweeping its bill through the shallow seawater. It breeds in Holland, southern Spain, the Balkans and across Asia from Turkey to China.

Opposite: **Little Bittern** *(Ixobrychus minutus)*, L 35 cm. Because of its skulking habits this small heron-like bird is frequently overlooked during its passage in spring and autumn. It is usually found in dense vegetation at fresh water margins and may sometimes be seen climbing about in reed beds. The bird shown here is a female and was observed expertly catching dragonflies (CWTP)

Little Stint *(Calidris minuta)*, L 13 cm. Having bred in the northern tundra of Europe and Asia, this tiny wader migrates south to winter in the Mediterranean and the Gulf. Apart from its size, it is best recognised by its black legs and straight black bill (CWTP)

Snipe *(Gallinago gallinago)*, L 27 cm. This bird's favourite haunts are inland water and reed-beds. The very long straight bill and bold stripes on the head and back aid in identifying this species (CWTP)

During the winter months some of the species that are seen on the coast also frequent the few fresh-water pools in Kuwait along with a number of other species. Snipe *(Gallinago gallinago)* and the smaller Jack Snipe *(Lymnocryptes minimus)* are regularly seen feeding in shallow pools where Dunlin, Little Stint *(Calidris minuta)*, Ringed Plovers and Kentish Plovers *(Charadrius alexandrinus)* are common. In the reeds at some pools the Moorhen *(Gallinula chloropus)*, a member of the Rallidae, breeds successfully and numbers of Coots *(Fulica atra)*, which are close relatives, may also occur. A few other members of the Rallidae, namely the Little Crake *(Porzana parva)*, Spotted Crake *(Porzana porzana)* and Water Rail *(Rallus*

White Wagtail *(Motacilla alba alba)*, L 18 cm. This small black and white bird is easily identified by its relatively long tail, which is repeatedly wagged up and down, and by its rapid walking gait (WAS)

Marsh Sandpiper *(Tringa stagnatilis)*, L 23 cm. Its long legs, slender straight bill and graceful movements make this one of the most attractive sandpipers to winter at freshwater pools in Kuwait (CWTP)

Wood Sandpiper *(Tringa glareola)*, L 20 cm. Shanks and sandpipers present difficulties in identification. The Wood Sandpiper is no exception and shows only slightly less contrast between upper and lower parts as compared with the Green Sandpiper (LC)

aquaticus) are recorded irregularly but as they are all very shy, retiring birds it is possible that they are frequently overlooked. Three species of the grebe family (Podicipitidae) also occur irregularly. In winter plumage they are all fairly drab, having dark grey upper- and pale underparts but they are readily separated by size. The Great Crested Grebe *(Podiceps cristatus)* with a length of 48 cm is half as big again as the Black-necked Grebe *(Podiceps nigricollis)*, which in turn is slightly larger than the Little Grebe *(Tachybaptus ruficollis)*. All three species have also been sighted at different times on calm coastal waters in the vicinity of Shuwaikh port.

Black-headed Gull *(Larus ridibundus)*, L 36 cm. This young gull is beginning to lose the brown colouration characteristic of the immature plumage. In winter, the red bill and legs help to distinguish this gull from the commoner Slender-billed Gull *(L. genei)* (CWTP)

Cormorants *(Phalacrocorax carbo)*, L 90 cm. Unlikely to be confused with any other sea-bird, these large, white-fronted diving birds are a common sight on the fishing traps and rocks along Kuwait City's seafront (CWTP)

One of the most numerous and widespread of Kuwait's winter visitors is the White Wagtail *(Motacilla alba alba)*, which is common around the permanent pools. Along with the White Wagtail at pools is the Water Pipit *(Anthus spinoletta spinoletta)*, but despite being the commonest pipit of winter months it is more localised than the wagtail. A few warblers, mainly Chiffchaffs *(Phylloscopus collybita)* and Whitethroats *(Sylvia communis)*, are also to be seen during the winter months.

One of the commonest sights around Kuwait City's coast at this time of the year is the Cormorants *(Phalacrocorax carbo)* sitting on the fish traps or flying in skeins across the bay. These are true winter visitors, arriving in considerable numbers within a period of a few days and departing as suddenly at the end of February or beginning of March. Soon after their departure a summer visitor, the Socotra Cormorant *(Phalacrocorax nigrogularis)*, arrives from the south. However, the species is not numerous in Kuwait and is to be found only along the more southerly coasts and not in Kuwait Bay.

Gulls, of course, can be seen at any time of the year but recognising the species in juvenile or winter plumage is not easy. The most common

Slender-billed Gulls *(Larus genei)*, L 43 cm. A small flock of gulls is seen here basking in early spring sunshine. The birds are mainly in winter plumage but two individuals to the right of the centre already have the red legs and bill of the breeding plumage (WAS)

species during the winter months are the Black-headed Gull *(Larus ridibundus)*, the Herring Gull *(Larus argentatus)*, the Lesser Black-backed *(Larus fuscus)* and the Slender-billed Gull *(Larus genei)*. Occasionally one can see a Great Black-headed Gull *(Larus ichthyaetus)* in its winter plumage. It is about the size and colouring of a Herring Gull but has dark smudges on its head and neck and greenish legs.

Reef Heron *(Egretta gularis schistacea)*, L 56 cm. This dark form of the eastern race of the Reef Heron is very common along the seashore. Both white and dark forms can be distinguished from the Little Egret *(E. garzetta)* by the yellow bill (CWTP)

Before leaving the coast a mention must be made of the Grey Herons *(Ardea cinerea)* and Reef Herons *(Egretta gularis schistacea)*, which are seen there at most times of the year. As it is unlikely that these birds breed in Kuwait they must be visitors. It is possible that the herons seen during the winter months move northwards in the spring and that their place is taken by others moving into Kuwait from the south. Grey Herons are absent during May and rare in April, June and July.

In the desert regions there are few regular winter visitors or residents but the most common must be the Lesser Short-toed Lark *(Calandrella cinerea)*, which sometimes occurs in large flocks as a winter visitor. Crested Larks *(Galerida cristata)* are

Isabelline Wheatear *(Oenanthe isabellina)*, L 16.5 cm. One of the larger wheatears to occur in Kuwait, this species can be seen from autumn through to spring. Its pale sandy colouring and absence of facial and throat markings help in distinguishing it from the males of all other wheatears (CWTP)

Stonechat *(Saxicola torquata)*, L 12.5 cm. Conspicuous white neck patches and an all black head are the distinguishing features of this chat. It may be found in urban areas, by inland water and in flat, open desert (WAS)

always in evidence and like Desert Larks *(Ammomanes deserti)* they are resident and breed here. Kuwait represents the eastern limits of distribution of the Temminck's Horned Lark *(Eremophila bilopha)*, which occurs across Arabia and the northern desert regions of North Africa as far west as Algeria. This attractive little desert bird can be seen in the west of the country. The largest lark of the region, the Hoopoe Lark *(Alaemon alaudipes)*, is a resident here and can therefore be seen throughout the year. Its name derives from the long down-curved bill and black and white wing pattern that is so Hoopoe-like in flight.

Several wheatears can be seen in the desert during the winter and a fairly common visitor to the wilder rocky parts is the Mourning Wheatear *(Oenanthe lugens)*. Unless one can glimpse the orange-brown marking under the tail this bird is difficult to distinguish from its close relative the Pied Wheatear *(Oenanthe pleschanka)*, but the latter is much less common at this time of year. One of the larger wheatears, the Isabelline Wheatear *(Oenanthe isabellina)*, is found in desert areas but it also occurs in cultivated areas including parks and gardens.

Finally, in this section dealing with the winter months, the gardens and parks must be considered. The Song Thrush *(Turdus philomelos)* is not

Mourning Wheatear *(Oenanthe lugens)*, L 13.5 cm. Sometimes called the Mourning Chat, this wheatear is to be found in wadis and remote rocky parts of the desert. It closely resembles the Pied Wheatear *(O. pleschanka)* but has orange-brown under tail coverts (WAS)

uncommon most winters and sometimes Robins
(Erithacus rubecula) and Blackbirds *(Turdus
merula)* occur here. One of the most attractive
winter visitors is the Bluethroat *(Luscinia svecica)*,
a rather retiring, but occasionally noisy, robin-like
bird. Stonechats *(Saxicola torquata)* are more bold
and are to be seen in gardens, near pools and on
larger bushes in the coastal desert regions.
Isabelline Shrikes *(Lanius isabellinus)* and the
larger Great Grey Shrikes *(Lanius excubitor)* may
also be seen sitting in prominent situations. These
birds are predators and eat a wide variety of
insects, small birds and lizards. Winter visitors that
have been recorded for Kuwait but are not often
seen include the Chaffinch *(Fringilla coelebs)*,
Brambling *(Fringilla montifringilla)*, Lapwing
(Vanellus vanellus), Houbara Bustard
(Chlamydotis undulata) and Short-eared Owl *(Asio
flammeus)*.

Lastly, mention must be made of the growing
population of Starlings *(Sturnus vulgaris)*.
Increasingly, Starlings are becoming part of the
general winter scene in Kuwait and the arrival of
one to two thousand birds at their roost in trees
near the Sheraton Hotel on a winter's evening can
be a spectacular sight.

Red-throated Pipit *(Anthus cervinus)*, L 14.5 cm. In breeding plumage this
pipit is easily distinguished by its reddish throat and breast (CWTP)

In Spring

Towards the end of February the spring migration
will begin and from then until April or May one
will notice many Swallows *(Hirundo rustica)* and
other members of the Hirundinidae moving northwards. A feature of migration that is common to
many species is well illustrated by these birds.
Individuals that are going through Kuwait in
February are probably travelling much further
north to their breeding grounds than those that

Yellow Wagtails *(Motacilla flava)*, L 16.5 cm. The Yellow Wagtail is a markedly variable species and on migration through Kuwait small groups comprised of several races may frequently be seen. During the spring migration, when the birds are in breeding plumage, the races are more easily discriminated. Here two female Sykes' *(M.f. beema)* are flanked by two males on the right of the picture and a Kirghiz Steppe *(M.f. lutea)* on the left (CWTP)

Grey Wagtail *(Motacilla cinerea)*, L 18 cm. Although resembling the yellow wagtails, the Grey can readily be told apart by its blue-grey upper parts. The female, pictured here, lacks the distinctive black throat of the male (CWTP)

pass through later. Along with the Swallows are Sand Martins *(Riparia riparia)* and small numbers of House Martins *(Delichon urbica)* and Red-rumped Swallows *(Hirundo daurica)*. During March and April another member of this family, the Crag Martin *(Hirundo rupestris)*, arrives and it is likely that this bird frequents large, cliff-like buildings in Kuwait when it stops over to feed on its northward journey. This is one of the species that is much more rarely seen in the autumn, indicating that it performs a loop-migration.

It is quite usual to see members of the swift family (Apodidae) travelling with the hirundines. Large numbers of Swifts *(Apus apus)* are normally seen but their very similar relative, the Pallid Swift *(Apus pallidus)*, is less common. Occasionally, both the largest and smallest swifts of the region occur here. With a wingspan of 53 cm, the Alpine Swift *(Apus melba)* is considerably larger than its relatives and being the only one with white under-parts it is easily recognised. The House Swift or Little Swift *(Apus affinis)* is the smallest of the family and the only member with a short, square tail.

Superficially the swallows, martins and swifts resemble each other quite closely and as they often occur in mixed flocks, wheeling and diving rapidly after flying insects, it is easy to fail to notice the one or two individuals that are different. Careful and patient observation of such flocks is often rewarded by identification of the occasional un-common species.

The White Wagtails, which have been such a feature of the winter scene in Kuwait, will also be moving away and the last ones will have gone by the middle of April, not to be seen again until about the middle of October. During the period from mid-February to mid-March the Grey Wagtail *(Motacilla cinerea)*, which is recognised by its blue-grey upperparts, yellow breast and very long tail, passes through Kuwait in small numbers. Various races or varieties of the yellow Wagtail are numerous and the Kirghiz Steppe race *(Motacilla flava lutea)* is especially attractive with its bright yellow head and body. The Water Pipit is still to be seen and will be changing into its breeding plumage but from the end of April another attrac-tive pipit, the Red-throated Pipit *(Anthus cer-vinus)*, will be abundant. This bird occasionally frequents parks and gardens around Kuwait City and Ahmadi but it prefers pools and grassy areas.

Steppe Buzzard *(Buteo buteo vulpinus)*, L 51-57 cm. Because of the extremely variable plumage the buzzard-sized birds of prey are easily confused with one another. A good view of the underwing markings and tail bars is essential for identification (WAS)

Steppe Eagle *(Aquila rapax orientalis)*, L 65-77 cm. Migrating Steppe Eagles provide a dramatic sight for the birdwatcher in Kuwait. The conspicuous white band along the rear edge of the underwing coverts is typical of the juvenile plumage (WAS)

Booted Eagle *(Hieraaetus pennatus)*, L 46-53 cm. In its more common light phase, shown here, this is one of the more easily identifiable larger raptors. The flight feathers appear black and contrast strikingly with the creamy white under wing-coverts and body (LC)

Black Kite *(Milvus migrans)*, L 56 cm. This bird of prey is one of the more common visitors and passage migrants. It has an overall dark appearance, long angular wings and a slightly forked tail which help in its identification (WAS).

Steppe Eagle *(Aquila rapax orientalis)*, L 65-77 cm. It may take several years for individuals of this species to achieve the near-black plumage of this mature adult (WAS)

Opposite: **Kestrel** *(Falco tinnunculus)*, L 34 cm. Most often spotted as it hovers stationary on rapidly beating wings, this falcon is probably the most common raptor here. The male differs from that of the Lesser Kestrel in having the red-brown upper parts spotted with black and a grey-blue forewing (WAS)

This time of the year brings one of Kuwait's spectacular ornithological events, the spring passage of the birds of prey. During the winter there will have been a few Kestrels *(Falco tinnunculus)* and Sparrowhawks *(Accipiter nisus)* and occasional Steppe *(Buteo buteo vulpinus)* and Long-legged *(Buteo rufinus)* Buzzards. However, in March it is very exciting to observe large numbers of eagles in their effortless flight soaring in thermals (rising columns of warmer air) to gain height and then gliding on swept-back wings to the next thermal. The large majority of the eagles are Steppe Eagles *(Aquila rapax orientalis)* but the much smaller Booted Eagle *(Hieraaetus pennatus)* is fairly common. Bonelli's Eagles *(Hieraaetus fasciatus)* and Spotted Eagles *(Aquila clanga)* as well as the larger Imperial Eagle *(Aquila heliaca)* also pass through Kuwait in small numbers at this time. Since birds of prey, especially the larger ones, rely mainly on soaring and gliding as their mode of travel, the eagles, vultures and buzzards will rest during the night when air temperatures are cooler. It is therefore sometimes possible to see eagles on the ground, generally on small hillocks, cliffs or higher ground. If left undisturbed, they will not leave until the sun is well up and thermals have formed above surface structures, such as barren rock, that heat the air immediately above them quicker than their surroundings. If the weather is suitable, these large raptors will be flying at great heights and this must be one of the reasons why the passage of such large numbers of Steppe Eagles had not been reported from Kuwait until two or three years ago.

The Steppe Eagle breeds in central Asia and is the eastern race of the Tawny Eagle *(Aquila rapax)*. It migrates to Africa, wintering in Ethiopia, central or southern Africa and, until recently, has been virtually unobserved on migration. For this reason the carefully recorded sightings of the Ahmadi Natural History Group are of sufficient importance to have been reported to the British Museum.

Another group of birds of prey that can be seen at this time is the Harriers and all four species of the region occur in Kuwait. The largest is the Marsh Harrier *(Circus aeruginosus)* and the smallest and least common is the Montagu's Harrier *(Circus pygargus)*. Both of the intermediate-sized relatives, the Hen Harrier *(Circus cyaneus)* and the Pallid Harrier *(Circus macrourus)*, are common and, like the other two species, occur in most localities. They characteristically hunt by flying rapidly and low across the ground and feed on a wide variety of small mammals, birds and insects.

Several members of the Falconidae pass through the country but, apart from the Kestrel and Lesser Kestrel *(Falco naumanni)*, none is very common. Indeed, the Hobby *(Falco subbuteo)* and the Peregrine *(Falco peregrinus)* are fairly rare and in the case of the Lanner Falcon *(Falco biarmicus)* some observers believe that only escaped falconers' birds have ever been seen. Escaped Saker Falcons *(Falco cherrug)* have also been noted but occasional passage migrants occur too.

Also rare here, or at least uncommon in the case of the small Egyptian Vulture *(Neophron percnopterus)*, are a few members of the group of

Marsh Harrier *(Circus aeruginosus)* , L 48-56 cm. All four of the European harriers occur in Kuwait and are often seen gliding low over the ground with slightly up-sloping wings hunting small animals. The pale head and obvious shoulder patch on an otherwise all-brown plumage indicates that this is an adult female (MS)

Honey Buzzard *(Pernis apivorus)* , L 52-60 cm. The name of this bird derives from its habit of robbing the nests of bees and wasps (WAS)

vultures. Both the Black Vulture *(Aegypius monachus)* and the Griffon Vulture *(Gyps fulvus)*, which are huge birds of prey, have been sighted irregularly. Much more common is the Osprey *(Pandion haliaetus)*, the only fish-hunting raptor to visit Kuwait. This is one of the most distinctive birds of prey, with its white head and underparts contrasting with the dark brown face and upperparts. It is more common in the autumn than spring and is usually seen at the coast, although it does frequent freshwater pools here.

At the other end of the size scale there are many smaller birds to be seen in springtime. Considerable numbers of warblers are present; some will have spent the winter in Kuwait, but

Ortolan Bunting *(Emberiza hortulana)* , L 16.5 cm. Small flocks of this attractive bunting may be seen during the spring and autumn migrations. The yellow of the chin and throat and the yellowish-white eye ring are distinctive features (CWTP)

most will be passage migrants. It is much easier to see Chiffchaffs here than is normally possible in Europe where they are usually heard singing from the middle of a thick bush but are rarely seen. In Kuwait they cannot hide so easily, and since they are not breeding they do not sing but call to each

Blackcap *(Sylvia atricapilla)* , L 14 cm. This little warbler is identified by the jet-black cap of the male and the reddish brown crown of the female. Being a passage migrant the Blackcap is seen during spring and autumn, usually in parks and gardens (CWTP)

Spotted Flycatcher *(Muscicapa striata)* , L 14 cm. This inconspicuous, small bird usually catches the eye as it launches from a favourite perch to give chase to a flying insect (CWTP)

Red-backed Shrike *(Lanius collurio)* , L 17 cm. All of the shrikes have the habit of impaling their victims on thorns or sharp spikes and storing them in a 'larder'. This is illustrated here by a female Red-backed Shrike, which has impaled a small bird to be eaten later (WAS)

other with a single note. There are several races of the Chiffchaff and several colour variations are to be seen in Kuwait. Some are brown to dark brown, whilst others are greyer. All can be distinguished by the dark colour of their legs from the very similar but less common Willow Warbler (*Phylloscopus trochilus*). Many other warblers pass through Kuwait, but are generally to be seen only in selected locations such as reed-beds and pools. One warbler, the Desert Warbler (*Sylvia nana*), is also present during the winter and can be seen in bushes and shrubs for instance along the Zor Ridge. An interesting observation is that the Desert Warbler often accompanies another bird such as a wheatear. More surprisingly the larger bird is sometimes a shrike and it seems strange to see a Great Grey Shrike followed from bush to bush by a Desert Warbler, a bird that could well be prey to the shrike. Although it does not breed here, the Desert Warbler is also one of the few birds in Kuwait that sings and this is a very pleasing sound in a desert area.

Redstart *(Phoenicurus phoenicurus)*, L 14 cm. An attractive robin-like bird, the Redstart is a passage migrant. The striking breeding plumage of the male is shown here but the red rump and tail are also shared by the female (CWTP)

In the desert during the spring one might be lucky enough to see a group of Caspian Plovers (*Charadrius asiaticus*) in their striking breeding plumage. They are birds of the open grassy plains of central Asia, but migrate through Kuwait. In the autumn they are much less colourful, having lost their breeding plumage. In addition to the *Charadrius* plovers already mentioned the Little Ringed Plover (*Charadrius dubius*) and the Grey Plover (*Pluvialis squatarola*) are quite common. The White-tailed Plover (*Vanellus leucurus*) is a fairly frequent visitor and two other *Vanellus* plovers, the Lapwing and the Red-wattled Plover (*Vanellus indicus*) are occasionally sighted. Dotterel (*Eudromias morinellus*) and Golden Plovers (*Pluvialis apricaria*) are uncommon visitors.

Whinchat (*Saxicola rubetra*), L 12.5 cm. Chats are small, perky robin-like thrushes often seen perching on a prominent outlook. The conspicuous broad whitish eyestripe distinguishes it from the Stonechat, a bird of similar habits and haunts (CWTP)

Masked Shrike (*Lanius nubicus*), L 17 cm. The plumage of this attractive shrike is mainly black and white. Its conspicuous white forehead prevents confusion with the Woodchat Shrike, which also differs in its rich chestnut crown and nape (LC)

Opposite: **Barred Warbler** (*Sylvia nisoria*), L 15 cm. An uncommon passage migrant, this is one of the larger *Sylvia* warblers seen in Kuwait. The fierce yellow eyes and bluish-grey plumage with obvious barring are characteristic of the male (CWTP)

Ringed Plover *(Charadrius hiaticula)* , L 19 cm. Out of the breeding season the striking markings of this medium-sized wader are lost and it then becomes difficult to distinguish between the six *Charadrius* plovers that occur here (CWTP)

Caspian Plover *(Charadrius asiaticus)* , L 19 cm. When seen on its spring migration northwards, this plover has handsome markings in the plumage. As its name implies, this plover breeds around the Caspian Sea (IW)

Great Reed Warbler *(Acrocephalus arundinaceus)* , L 19 cm. All the species of reed warbler have very similar plumage, that is uniformly brown on the upper parts and pale beneath. Being easily the largest of the region, the Great Reed Warbler is probably best recognised by its size (CWTP)

Bittern *(Botaurus stellaris)*, L 76 cm. When alarmed or on the alert, this large heron adopts the head-up posture shown here. It is a shy bird preferring freshwater habitats with plenty of vegetation for cover (WAS)

Spring also brings some of the most colourful birds to be seen in Kuwait. European Bee-eaters *(Merops apiaster)* and Blue-cheeked Bee-eaters *(Merops superciliosus)* are often heard before being seen for they constantly utter their call-note whilst hunting insects on the wing. Sometimes they occur in quite large mixed flocks especially in the evening when they arrive in the suburbs to roost in trees. The European Bee-eater winters in tropical Africa and migrates to the Mediterranean countries and western Asia. April in the spring and August and September in the autumn are the best months for seeing these species but, because they do not travel very far north, they have been seen during all the months from February to December.

Another colourful bird that is seen at the same time as the Bee-eaters is the Hoopoe *(Upupa epops)*. This species is widespread, some individuals being sedentary and other migratory. Those birds that breed in Europe and western Asia winter in Africa and southern Asia. The food of this bird is large insects such as locusts, larvae of large beetles, crickets and spiders, lizards and other small animals.

Little Ringed Plover *(Charadrius dubius)*, L 19 cm. This small plover is easily confused with its close relative the Ringed Plover, which is illustrated on the opposite page. The Little Ringed has a yellow eye ring, mainly blackish bill and a white line between the crown and the black forehead (WAS)

Opposite: **White-tailed Plover** *(Vanellus leucurus)*, L 28 cm. Having soft-brown and white plumage, long yellow legs and a conspicuous white rump, this large plover is fairly easily recognised. Usually it is seen close to fresh water (WAS)

Hoopoe *(Upupa epops)* L 28 cm. Whether seen with the crest forward and raised or folded down, the pinkish-cinnamon plumage with strong black and white bars makes this bird unmistakable (WAS)

Squacco Heron *(Ardeola ralloides)*, L 46 cm. In flight this small heron appears white but the plumage is actually tawny-buff. This bird is shown in its breeding plumage with black streaked crown and crest (CWTP)

Both rollers of the region, the Roller *(Coracias garrulus)* and the Indian Roller *(Coracias benghalensis)*, are found in Kuwait and like the Hoopoe, these species winter in the East Africa savannah regions. The Roller is most frequently seen during the autumn migration, which is under way as early as July, but it may also be seen throughout March to May. Its relative, the Indian Roller, is much less common and is more likely to be sighted during the winter months.

Since spring is also the time for breeding, it is appropriate to consider those birds that are hardy enough to nest in Kuwait. The most common is, of course, the House Sparrow *(Passer domesticus)*, which seems able to continue breeding throughout the year. At least, nests are occupied during every month of the year. As a group, the larks are probably the next most successful breeding birds in Kuwait. The Crested Lark is common throughout the year and typically it nests under a bush. It is a bird that breeds throughout central and southern Europe, parts of Africa and central Asia and as far east as Korea. The Desert Lark certainly breeds in Kuwait and on rocky ground it will sometimes surround its nest with pebbles and even lay out a

European Bee-eaters *(Merops apiaster)*, L 28 cm. Without doubt these are Kuwait's most colourful birds. Usually they are seen in flocks flying swallow-like after bees and wasps or perched on telegraph wires or bushes or low trees (CWTP)

Opposite: **Roller** *(Coracias garrulus)*, L 31 cm. This handsome bird is commonly seen in cultivated localities and areas of flattish scrub during the spring and autumn months (LC)

Lapwing *(Vanellus vanellus)*, L 30 cm. This plover is easily identified by its general pied appearance and the prominent upturned crest (WAS)

Bimaculated Lark *(Melanocorypha bimaculata)*, L 16.5 cm. The robust build and heavy seed-eating bill is typical of the Calandra larks. Although it is not common, this lark has been known to breed in Kuwait (CWTP)

Crested Lark *(Galerida cristata)*, L 17 cm. Seen in most localities, this lark is another of the few resident species. Although the heavily streaked plumage is similar to that of other larks found here, the permanently erected crest makes for easy identification (JB)

path of pebbles to the nest, a device which protects the nest from the wind. This bird has another interesting habit, in summer it is often found sheltering from the heat in the hole of the Dhub *(Uromastyx microlepis)*. The largest lark of the region, the Hoopoe Lark, also breeds regularly in Kuwait. With its black and white wings and distinctive display flight, it is a most attractive

desert bird. It has a very melodious song, which can be heard from some distance. The number of eggs varies from two to four, depending on the dryness of the weather. Although the Bimaculated Lark *(Melanocorypha bimaculata)* is not common in Kuwait it has recently been discovered to breed here. Another lark that is found in the higher desert regions along the Wadi Al-Baten in the west is the Temminck's Horned Lark. This species is present throughout the year and is known to nest here. In this same area, the Bar-tailed Desert Lark *(Ammomanes cincturus)* and the Thick-billed Lark *(Rhamphocorys clot-bey)* have been seen, but it is

Black-crowned Finch Lark *(Eremopterix nigriceps)*, L 11 cm. A heavy bill and finch-like form give this member of the lark family its name. The male is instantly recognisable by his black crown and all black underparts (LC)

Blue-cheeked Bee-eater *(Merops superciliosus)*, L 31 cm. Similar in habits to the more colourful European Bee-eater, the two are often seen flying in mixed flocks. However, the Blue-cheeked is easily distinguished by its overall green appearance and its longer central tail feathers (CWTP)

not certain that they breed. Similarly, little is known of the nesting habits of the Black-crowned Finch-Lark *(Eremopterix nigriceps)*, a summer visitor that possibly breeds here. This is a very attractive species in which the male only is boldly marked in black, white and brown all through the year.

Eagle Owls *(Bubo bubo)* are known to be resident in the more remote regions of the Wadi Al-Baten, and during the past three years a nest has been located. This is a spectacular, handsome bird and it is to be hoped that it will continue to nest in Kuwait. The Little Owl *(Athene noctua)* is usually to be seen in the gullies of the Zor Ridge and although there is no firm evidence that it breeds there, this is almost certain judging by the behaviour of these birds. A bird that definitely breeds in small numbers in the gullies of the Zor Ridge is the Brown-necked Raven *(Corvus ruficollis)*. This is the desert version of the Raven and it occurs in the Sahara, across Arabia and as far east as the Thar Desert in north-western India. Another bird found in the desert areas and known to breed there is the Cream-coloured Courser

Eagle Owl chick *(Bubo bubo)*. It is not uncommon in this species for eggs in the same clutch to hatch at different times depending on food supply. However, only the one owlet, pictured here, was raised in this instance. The gerbil at the back of the nest will provide a future meal for the chick (CWTP)

Opposite: **Cream-coloured Coursers** *(Cursorius cursor)*, L 23 cm. At the approach of danger this bird will often run and crouch rather than fly away. The speckled sandy-cream plumage indicates that these are juvenile birds (WAS)

Moorhens *(Gallinula chloropus)*, L 33 cm. Representing another of the few resident species, these Moorhens belonged to a colony of more than 30 birds. They are usually found by fresh water where there is plenty of vegetation to provide cover (CWTP)

163

White-eared Bulbul *(Pycnonotus leucogenys)*, L 18 cm. One of the few resident species, this bulbul is locally common in parks and gardens (CWTP)

Opposite: **Black-winged Stilt** *(Himantopus himantopus)*, L 38 cm. This is another unmistakable visitor, easily recognised by its extremely long pink legs, black and white plumage and long straight black bill (WAS)

Kentish Plover *(Charadrius alexandrinus)*, L 16 cm. Photographed in the spring, this bird was calling to its two chicks. Unlike the two Ringed Plovers, the legs are black and the black breast-band does not form a complete ring (CWTP)

(Cursorius cursor). Sometimes young birds are also to be seen on the beach and by fresh water in the summer. Broken eggs, probably from hatchings, have been found under trees frequented by Collared Doves *(Streptopelia decaocto)* so it is fairly certain that they also breed in Kuwait. An unexpected breeding bird for Kuwait is the Moorhen, and at one site up to a hundred birds have been estimated to be present. They have been seen throughout the year and immature birds are commonly seen in the summer months. Formerly, several terns were known to breed on Kuwait's off-shore islands but the present breeding status of some of these birds is not known. The only birds that definitely raise young on or near to the shore are the Kentish Plover and Crab Plover.

In Summer

This now brings us to a consideration of the summer months in Kuwait. The conditions will vary greatly from one year to another depending on the rainfall in the previous winter and spring. Even so, they are always harsh with high temperatures and an average of forty days of dust storms. In early summer the humidity can be very low, but during August it is not unknown to have temperatures of 48 - 50° C and humidity of 80 - 100 %. For this reason many birds are absent during June and July but there are a few hardy summer visitors. The Black-crowned Finch Lark has already been mentioned and possibly the most unlikely summer visitor is the Rufous Bushchat

Terns. Pictured here is a yellow-billed Lesser Crested Tern *(Sterna bengalensis)*, L 36 cm, with two Sandwich Terns *(Sterna sandvicensis)*, L 41 cm. Several species of tern, including the Lesser Crested, breed on islands in the Gulf (WAS)

Rufous Bushchat *(Cerocotrichas galactotes syriacus)* , L 15 cm. Known also as the Rufous Warbler,this bird is unusual in being a summer visitor. Less secretive than warblers, it frequents parks and gardens, inland water and semi-desert habitats. The long rufous tail with its distinct black and white tip is characteristically raised and fanned. It is possible that some birds breed here (CWTP)

Garganey *(Anas querquedula)*, L 38 cm. This passage migrant is one of the smallest surface-feeding or dabbling ducks and during both spring and autumn it is commonly sighted on inland fresh water ponds. The conspicuous white stripe over the eye is a definitive feature for identification of the drake (CWTP)

(Cercotrichas galactotes syriacus). This charming bird seems to take the place of the Bluethroat as the latter departs for the summer and although it is really a warbler, with its large size, long legs and stance it resembles a thrush. Its range covers southern Europe, the northern half of Africa, except the deserts, and south-west Asia. It arrives in Kuwait in April and is gone by the end of August or middle of September. In May it may be heard singing from a bush and though its display flight has been observed there is no other evidence that it breeds here. Some of the terns, for example the Swift Tern *(Sterna bergii)*, Lesser Crested Tern *(Sterna bengalensis)*, White-cheeked Tern *(Sterna repressa)* and Bridled Tern *(Sterna anaethetus)*, are summer visitors. As mentioned earlier, some or all of these terns may have bred on Kuwait's islands, but there have been no authenticated records of breeding for the past few years.

In Autumn

The autumn migration starts earlier than was previously suspected and August is the best month for seeing certain birds. These are generally those birds that have not travelled very far north and, having nested, are returning to their normal quarters. A good example is the Black-winged Stilt *(Himantopus himantopus)*, which is more plentiful in the spring but is often missed on its return since few people bird-watch in August. Of course, a few are seen in September and October. The birds of prey also start their return journey at this time but continue through until late November. With many birds, the adults often travel before the younger birds and this is probably so with some birds of prey. The autumn passage of the Steppe Eagle may be particularly spectacular and recently over two hundred and fifty birds were seen in one week-end. Quite often a group of Steppe Eagles will be accompanied by one or two Kestrels and, when a column forms up in a thermal, the Kestrel is generally at the top.

Many of the younger birds that appear at this time do not have their full adult plumage and it is sometimes difficult to identify the race and even the species to which they belong. This is particularly true of the races of Yellow Wagtail and the various species of wheatear that occur in Kuwait. During autumn Wheatears *(Oenanthe oenanthe)* are common passage migrants and occur in most types of locality. Many Black-eared Wheatears *(Oenanthe hispanica)*, Desert Wheatears *(Oenanthe deserti)* and Red-tailed Wheatears *(Oenanthe xanthoprymna)* also pass southwards through the country but it is fairly common for some individuals of these three species to remain for the winter. The rarest wheatear to visit here is the Hume's Wheatear *(Oenanthe alboniger)* a bird that haunts remote rocky wadis.

Some of the ducks that pass through Kuwait such as the Teal *(Anas crecca)*, Garganey *(Anas querquedula)* and Mallard *(Anas platyrhynchos)*, seem to be more common during the autumn than in the spring. A few other ducks are as common on the spring migration and these include the Pintail *(Anas acuta)*, Shoveler *(Anas clypeata)* and the less often seen Gadwall *(Anas strepera)* and Pochard *(Aythya ferina)*. On rare occasions the Tufted Duck *(Aythya fuligula)* passes through Kuwait. During the last five years small flocks of Shelduck *(Tadorna tadorna)* have spent the winter months in the bay at Sulaibikhat.

Pintail *(Anas acuta)* , L 56 cm. Seen on both freshwater pools and the coast, the Pintail is a common winter visitor and passage migrant. The drake's tail feathers are even more elongated than those of the duck shown here (WAS)

Opposite: **Teal** *(Anas crecca)*, L 35 cm. This, the smallest duck of the region, is a common winter visitor. The horizontal white line above the wing and the creamy-yellow patch under the tail help to distinguish the drake in mixed flocks of resting or swimming ducks (CWTP)

Shoveler *(Anas clypeata)* , L 51 cm. Not surprisingly, the name of this surface-feeding duck derives from the heavy shovel-shaped bill. Against the colourful plumage of the drake shown here, the duck appears very drab but she too has a light blue forewing and green speculum that are especially noticeable in flight (CWTP)

Finally, as rarity itself often stimulates interest and even excitement, a mention will be made of a few more uncommon or occasional species that may be sighted in Kuwait. One bird that used to be a fairly common resident here but that has suffered almost complete extinction through uncontrolled hunting is the Houbara Bustard. It is a most impressive bird and can still be found on rare occasions in Kuwait. However, since most sightings are from near the borders it is probable that such birds have wandered only temporarily into the country.

A migrant from the Arctic that has been seen on several occasions recently and that might not be as rare in Kuwait as the records suggest is the Temminck's Stint *(Calidris temminckii)*. This tiny wader closely resembles the very common Little Stint but the two can be distinguished easily by the colour of their legs, which is pale yellow-green in the Temminck's and black in the Little Stint. However, as both these birds are only 13 cm long and are often encountered wading in muddy water, the difference may easily go unnoticed. The Temminck's Stint therefore may have been overlooked on previous occasions.

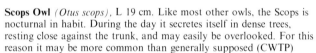

Scops Owl *(Otus scops)*, L 19 cm. Like most other owls, the Scops is nocturnal in habit. During the day it secretes itself in dense trees, resting close against the trunk, and may easily be overlooked. For this reason it may be more common than generally supposed (CWTP)

Pin-tailed Sandgrouse *(Pterocles alchata)*, 37 cm. Most of the sandgrouse are colourful birds but this species is the only one with a white belly and is easily identified in flight. It prefers bushy and cultivated areas to open desert (MS)

Another species that may have been overlooked but for a different reason is the Scops Owl *(Otus scops)*. This small owl is active at night and during daylight it rests motionless in the dense foliage of trees, usually close against the trunk. In both its grey and brown forms the colouring is fairly cryptic and the bird may thus remain unobserved.

In winter, and more especially spring, the colourful and attractive Persian or White-throated Robin *(Irania gutturalis)* may be seen here. This species has a limited distribution, breeding in Iran, Syria and Turkey but small numbers migrate through Kuwait. A charming small bird that also occurs irregularly as a winter visitor is the Penduline Tit *(Remiz pendulinus)*, which is most likely to be seen in reed beds or close to freshwater pools.

Perhaps the most spectacular rarities are the Griffon Vulture and the Black Vulture. These huge birds of prey are highly adapted to soaring, having long broad wings with a span approaching 3 m in both species. They are usually spotted circling at great heights in open country as they scour the desert for carrion.

As indicated at the outset, this chapter on the birds of Kuwait is by no means comprehensive and many birds, indeed even whole families, have not been mentioned. However, the three field guides recommended at the end of this book will enable the interested reader to identify most of the species that will be encountered in Kuwait and the surrounding region.

White-throated Robin *(Irania gutturalis)*, L 16.5 cm. Also named the Persian Robin, this attractive bird passes through the Country on its migration. It is usually found amongst the bushes of rocky and stony wadis (WAS)

Mammals

By
David Clayton

The mammalian desert community is a surprisingly rich and varied one, but one group - the rodents - is particularly characteristic of arid regions the world over. The success in adapting to desert conditions is simply a reflection of the fact that the rodents are without doubt the most successful of modern mammals. In common with most desert mammals the rodents are paler than related species elsewhere and buff, greyish or sandy coats that enable the animals to blend in with their surroundings predominate. The coat also provides thermal protection by reflecting the heat. Desert rodents have adopted a more or less bipedal jumping form of locomotion as best exemplified by the Lesser Jerboa *(Jaculus jaculus)* which is found

Lesser Jerboa *(Jaculus jaculus)*. Equally at home in true desert sand or stony steppe, this is one of the most successful mammals of the region (DAC)

Sundevall's Jird *(Meriones crassus)*. The desert rodents are very wary and run for cover at the slightest sign of danger. In such circumstances it is extremely difficult to positively identify the animal (WAS)

Opposite: **Libyan Jird** *(Meriones libycus)*. This is the largest and one of the most social of Kuwait's rodents and lives in widespread colonies in areas where there are bushes and sandy hummocks (TCV)

in Kuwait in areas of level, barren terrain. These animals were first described by Herodotus 2000 years ago when he called them 'dipodes' or 'two-footed' and the name lives on today as the Family Dipodidae. Their spindly hind legs are over four times longer than the front legs. When hunting for seeds the jerboa walks on all four limbs, but at other times is bipedal. It also takes short hops whilst foraging but adopts a striding gait for faster movement. During flight from predators, however, both hind legs work together and the animal bounds along covering as much as 3 m in a single leap. Sudden changes of direction between leaps are accomplished with ease and can be attributed to bipedalism and an extremely long tail. Streaming out backwards on take-off and being raised on landing, the tail acts a counterpoise, rudder and brake during running. Whilst the animal is resting the tail acts as a prop. Most species of jerboa have a conspicuous tuft of hair, the significance of which is unknown, at the tip of the tail. In the Lesser Jerboa this tuft is white.

Like other desert rodents jerboas are nocturnal, spending the daylight hours underground in their burrows to avoid the rigorous surface conditions. Where other burrowing animals excavate a relatively simple tunnel, desert rodents build extremely complicated systems. There are usually several interconnecting tunnels, some blind, others open to the surface, often in the shade of a bush, in which case the tunnels are built amongst the bush's roots. The longer the occupation of these systems the more extensive they become, often having separate breeding chambers and food stores. Other blind tunnels will be emergency exits, ending just below the hard-crust surface layer of sand; originally open burrows, they have become filled with sand. Although not practised by the jerboas found in Kuwait, sealing of the main burrow exits, either at their entrance or inside the tunnels, is practised by many of the desert rodents. The Bedouin believe that this is to prevent snakes or warm air from entering. Certainly the burrow's micro-climate is markedly different from that of the surface, its main feature being its relative constancy in the face of wide external variation. Within the burrow the daily temperature change will only be a quarter of that of the surface whilst the relative humidity will be as much as five times as great. The rodents are able to control these conditions by modifying the length and depth of the tunnels, by varying the extent of the soil seal at the entrances and by taking plant material inside.

Being nocturnal, jerboas have large eyes but probably rely more on their acute sense of hearing for warning of predators. Having large external ears and enlarged bony capsules of the inner ears, the animal can detect the slightest sound made by an approaching predator. The movement of sand and vibrations set up by a ground predator or even the seemingly silent aerial approach of an owl can be detected by the alert jerboa. It is probable that the long hind legs evolved primarily to enable the animal to scan its surroundings for the approach of predators.

The slightly larger Euphrates Jerboa *(Allactaga euphratica)* is also found in Kuwait but is much rarer than the Lesser Jerboa. It is basically similar in appearance to the Lesser Jerboa but has five rather than three toes on its hind feet and has even larger ears. It is generally true that the ears, tails and feet of mammals living in hot areas are larger than those of mammals from colder climates and it is possible that the larger, relatively naked ears of desert mammals have the secondary function of heat exchangers. In the cool of the burrow the well vascularised ears will act like radiator fins and dissipate excess body heat. At times when it would be an embarrassment to lose heat, the animal simply sits on its feet, wraps the tail round its body and folds its ears.

The Family Cricetidae includes hampsters, voles, lemmings and, of more direct relevance to Kuwait, the jirds and gerbils. These latter animals are known to people throughout the world through the 'ambassador' of the group *Meriones unguiculatus* or the Mongolian Gerbil, which has become a firm favourite as a pet in the home. They are easy to look after, seldom bite when handled, are quite sociable and can subsist entirely on dry food. The latter attribute is obviously related to the animal's adaptation to life in arid lands. It is unfortunate, however, that the 'ambassador' was given the wrong name! Members of the Genus *Meriones* are jirds not gerbils, whilst gerbils are members of the Genus *Gerbillus* but in Kuwait both are represented.

The two local jirds, *Meriones crassus* and *Meriones lybicus,* are among the most social of Kuwait's rodents, living in widespread colonies in areas where there are sandy hummocks with tufts of

Hairy-footed Gerbil *(Gerbillus cheesmani)*. The characteristic naked tail of the species is clearly visible in these animals. Normally nocturnal, the heat of the day has prompted the individual on the right to cool itself by lying flat on the ground (TCV)

grass and low bushes. They are confined to such terrain because of the demands for food and protection from predators. Whilst resembling the jerboa, the jirds have shorter hind limbs and, lacking the jerboas' jumping powers, they can neither range so far in search of food nor rely on sustained rapid flight to escape predators.

In comparison with gerbils, the jirds are robust rodents with somewhat darker sandy brown fur. The largest of the jirds found in Kuwait is the Libyan Jird *(M. libycus)*. The head and body are about 13-15 cm long with a tail of equal length ending in a dark grey tuft. During the hottest part of the summer jirds are nocturnal, remaining in their burrows during the day. In some areas, however, they are strongly diurnal during the rest of the year but are usually only seen as they scurry back to their burrows with their tails held high in the air. Occasionally they make a ticking sound like two sticks being knocked together. This is a warning call given by the retreating individuals.

The distinguishing features of the second jird, Sundevall's Jird *(M. crassus)*, are its lighter coat, smaller ears and terminal tail tuft and markedly smaller hind feet. It is also found burrowing in sandy hummocks, which are usually covered by thorny bushes. This jird is nocturnal, feeding in the burrow on succulent twigs and seeds that it has collected whilst foraging.

It is presumed that the jirds' breeding season is during spring and early summer to coincide with the maximum availability of their food but it is possible that they also breed at other times. The brood chamber of the Libyan Jird is lined with shredded vegetable material whilst Sundevall's Jird has a preference for paper and cloth. In one aspect of their breeding the jirds and gerbils are unusual rodents: the males are involved in the rearing of the offspring and, in captivity at least, help their mates to keep the litter warm and retrieve any young that stray. More commonly, rodent males are driven away by the hostile females.

House Mouse *(Mus musculus)*. More commonly associated with man, this rodent is also found in the desert where its excellent powers of water conservation help to ensure its survival (WAS)

Of the three species of true gerbils in Kuwait, *Gerbillus cheesmani* or the Hairy-footed Gerbil is the easiest to recognise. It is a medium-sized gerbil with a sandy buff-coloured back. The distinctive features are the naked tail without a terminal tuft and the long hairs on the soles of the feet. This latter characteristic is equivalent to the fringed toes of the lizards and enables the animal to move more easily on loose sand. The other gerbils, *Gerbillus nanus* and *Gerbillus dasyrus,* have black tail tufts but no hairs on their feet. *G. nanus* is the smaller but more common of the two. The gerbils are strictly nocturnal, emerging from their burrows in the late evening. In general, whereas jirds eat the leaves and stalks or roots of desert plants, gerbils eat the seeds, enabling them to co-exist in the same localities.

Surprisingly, the House Mouse *(Mus musculus),* which is more commonly associated with man, is found in the desert sometimes as an occasional cohabitant of the burrow systems of gerbils and jirds. The very characteristics that ensured its long and successful exploitation of man-made environments also suit it to life in the desert. It is small, nocturnal and extremely agile and, more importantly, it can survive for long periods without drinking. Like the gerbils the House Mouse can live for months on a diet of dry seeds and its body can withstand marked dehydration. The success in surviving on dry seeds depends on having a burrow with relatively high humidity. This ensures that the animal looses little or no water through respiration and is able to exist on the water produced during the metabolism of dry food. The absence of sweat glands in desert rodents is another water conservation adaptation. Perspirative cooling requires considerable amounts of water not available to the desert dweller and nocturnal habits clearly obviate the need for such mechanisms. During forced exposure to the heat of the sun the rodent will attempt to cool itself by lying flat on the ground in shade. By pushing away the surface layer of sand the body can be pressed onto the cooler sub-surface layers. Under extreme stress the emergency mechanism of copious salivation operates. By wetting the fur of the head and neck the animal obtains some degree of cooling but, needless to say, this is effective only for a short time.

In Kuwait there are both wild and domestic populations of the House Mouse, but the other local members of the Muridae, the Brown and Black Rats, are strictly limited to human habitation and occur only accidentally in the desert. Unlike the House Mouse, domestic rats need plenty of drinking water and are unable to survive in arid regions. The Black Rat *(Rattus rattus)*, sometimes called the Ship Rat or Roof Rat, was for a long time a major pest in Europe. More recently, its position has been superseded by its larger relative the Brown Rat *(Rattus norvegicus)*. Changing building practices and sanitary facilities and the Brown Rat's greater aggressiveness all contributed to this change. In a much shorter period of time this sequence of events has also occurred in Kuwait where the replacement of thatch by tile and slate, of daub and wattle by brick and cement has reduced the number of habitats available for the black species. The introduction of underground sewage systems in the large modern city is extemely favourable to the Brown Rat but the government's careful control programme has succeeded in reducing the prevalence of this pest.

The commonest insectivore in Kuwait is *Hemiechinus auritus* or the Long-eared Hedgehog, so called because it has very large ears for its small body. The ears project well beyond the protective mantle of spines. These spines are black but for a wide sub-terminal white band, effectively giving the animal a pale sandy appearance. The lower flanks

Ethiopian Hedgehog *(Paraechinus aethiopicus)*. This handsome black-and-white faced animal is the common desert hedgehog found throughout Arabia. Being strictly nocturnal, however, it is rarely seen (AJS)

Long-eared Hedgehog *(Hemiechinus auritus)*. This hedgehog is found in the desert fringes or in cultivated land and avoids the rigours of the climate by burrowing (WAS)

and underbelly are covered with white fur. In Kuwait the salt cedar plantations are ideal habitats for this hedgehog since it is only a semi-desert animal, preferring shrubbed areas to the true desert. As nocturnal, burrowing animals that eat small invertebrates including insects, hedgehogs are well suited to living in arid regions and the second species found in Kuwait is a true desert inhabitant. The Ethiopian Hedgehog *(Paraechinus aethiopicus)* is a larger animal that also has big ears but that can easily be distinguished from the Long-eared Hedgehog by virtue of a V-shaped parting in the spines of the forehead, a black face and a median dark stripe across its back where the spines do not have the white band.

Closely related to the insectivores are the Chiroptera or bats. The two bats attributed to Kuwait are members of the suborder Microchiroptera, which includes the insect-eating and the vampire bats. These are the bats that navigate by echo-location. High frequency sounds are produced, which, when reflected back to the ear, enable the bat to detect objects in its surroundings. The system is very sensitive, enabling the bat to catch insect prey in flight and even to avoid thin wires. The insect is caught in a 'scoop net' formed by the wing membrane spread between the tail and hind limbs. The presence of bats in desert regions is entirely dependent on suitable daytime roosting sites such as caves, dark ruins or even crevices large enough to shelter them. Being nocturnal animals, they avoid the daytime heat of the desert but show no other special modification in relation to their environment. Severe drought and a decreased insect population may, however, cause them to migrate. Since there are no known large roosts in Kuwait, it is probable that most, if not all, bats in Kuwait are accidentals or migrants especially as the species seen are colonial. The Trident Leaf-nosed Bat *(Asellia tridens)* prefers dark ruins or dry caverns and is common in Iraq where there are large roosts. Specimens collected in Kuwait in recent years were found after severe dust-storms and were probably blown south from Iraq. These bats appear late at dusk and look pallid against the dark background. Their flight is low and swift and has the quality of a large butterfly. Kuhl's Pipistrelle *(Pipistrellus kuhli)* is a more likely resident and is the most abundant and ubiquitous bat in the middle eastern region, preferring crevices of walls and roofs of buildings for its roost. It may be seen abroad during warm evenings throughout the year and may fly out over the desert. The bat pictured here is a somewhat emaciated Naked-bellied Tomb Bat *(Taphozous nudiventris)*, which is also a colonial crevice-dwelling bat common in Iraq along the Tigris and Euphrates rivers. It is known for its seasonal migrations and it is possible that those from the middle Euphrates winter further south with occasional strays landing in Kuwait.

The only representative of the Lagomorpha (rabbits and hares) in Kuwait is the extremely adaptable Cape Hare *(Lepus capensis)*. It is the most widely distributed mammal in the Arabian peninsula and, as various subspecies or geographical races, is also found in much of Africa and Eurasia. With its long ears, well developed tail and long hind limbs it is easily distinguished from other Arabian mammals. If one finds only the remains, the hare's skull can be recognised immediately by the presence of two pairs of upper incisors, the

Naked-bellied Tomb Bat *(Taphozous nudiventris)*. This crevice-dwelling species is noted for its swift and strong flight and often travels considerable distances from the roost to hunt (ANHG)

Common Red Fox *(Vulpes vulpes)*. Although principally nocturnal in activity it is not unusual to see the fox abroad in the daytime. The desert dwelling populations subsist on small birds, mammals and reptiles including Dhub (WAS).

second nestling behind the much larger functional first pair: rodents have only one pair of upper incisors. Despite its wide distribution little is known of the hare in the Arabian peninsula but it can certainly live in areas where no free water is available. Unlike the gerbils, it requires green food to maintain a positive water balance. It is said that the hare does not burrow but merely seeks shade in depressions or beneath overhanging rocks. Individuals found in burrows may simply have appropriated them rather than built them. In other areas the animal is non-burrowing, simply having a surface lair where the young are born active, fully furred and with open eyes.

The wolf of this region *(Canis lupus)* is a large, heavily built canid whose form is more like that of a long-legged jackal than that of a wolf. Its relatively thick luxuriant coat is a uniform pale yellow-buff with a scattering of black over the back and tail. Preying on flocks of sheep and goats and even on man himself, the wolf is an ancient enemy of man in the Middle East. In arid regions these animals hunt singly, or at most in pairs, and show extreme cunning in their hunting technique. According to one account of sheep being taken from a Bedouin encampment at night, one wolf decoyed watchdogs away from the camp by approaching from upwind, whilst his mate stealthily circled round to enter the tent and drag away a full-grown sheep and its lamb. The wolves' spoor and the remains of the sheep were later found over two kilometres away.

Occasional hybridisation of wolves and feral dogs is a distinct possibility and distant sightings of wolves in Kuwait are, in the absence of any firmer evidence, more likely to be of feral dogs or hybrids than of wolves. The same mistake should not be made with regard to feral dogs and the foxes found in Kuwait. The Fennec Fox *(Fennecus zerda)* has an unmistakable beauty all its own and the Arabian form of the Common Red Fox *(Vulpes vulpes)* is clearly a fox. It has a slender build, relatively short legs, pointed muzzle, strikingly large ears and a long heavy brush. Individuals of the race found in the Arabian peninsula vary greatly in colour but, in common with other desert mammals, show an overall tendency to greater pallor compared with European races. The black flecking and reddish tint of the latter are missing and generally the fox is a pale sandy brown.

The Common Red Fox is a remarkably adaptable predator found in almost all available types of habitat in Arabia. In the escarpment area of Kuwait, the lair is found amongst the boulders and in rocky crevices whilst in sandier areas a simple earth is dug out of soft hummocks. Although the animal is principally nocturnal, daytime activity is not unusual and the fox may be seen lying out in patches of shrub during the day. Whilst avoiding man, the fox may frequent rubbish dumps and will even enter the town and gardens to prey on domestic livestock and to scavenge refuse. Desert populations subsist on small birds, mammals and reptiles.

By contrast, the Fennec Fox is a strictly desert inhabitant preferring sandy areas. This delightful fox is rare in the Arabian peninsula and, as much as one would wish otherwise, it is unlikely that there are any remaining in Kuwait. It is worth mentioning, however, if only because it exhibits a number of characteristics typical of a desert inhabitant. Being only 35-40 cm long, this tiny fox is much smaller than its relatives from temperate

Wild Cat *(Felis silvestris)*. Caught in the desert near Nuwaisib, this agile predator does not take kindly to captivity. Another nocturnal predator, the Wild Cat is probably more common than scarce records indicate (MS)

climates. It has well developed sense organs, large eyes and enormous ears, which act both as an aid to keen hearing and as a cooling device. The pale coat is a uniform brownish-buff and there is a black tip to the tail. The Fennec Fox typically spends the daylight hours in a burrow.

In common with the Fennec, the wolf and the hare, the following mammals have been recorded for Kuwait but are rarely seen nowadays. These too must be close to extinction in Kuwait but may occur in the border regions.

In some ways the Ratel or Honey Badger *(Mellivora capensis)* is a spectacular mammal with its distinctive black and white coat, tremendous incurving front claws and suffocatingly nauseous anal gland secretion, which can be detected over 50 m away. The Ratel is a short-legged, large-bodied beast able to exist in a wide variety of habitats including extremely arid terrain. It is predominantly nocturnal and subsists entirely on reptiles including the Dhub, which it is well equipped to unearth. Even in hard ground it can work its way underground in about ten minutes. As its name implies it will eat honey and bees when it can get them and in other parts of the world Honey-guide birds serve to direct their search. Whilst not aggressive by nature, the Ratel will fight with great courage when attacked, gaining protection from its extraordinarily tough, thick and mobile hide which is impenetrable even by the quills of porcupines or the fangs of venomous snakes. The Ratel's coat is predominantly black underneath and white on the back and flanks. The white mantle begins as a pure white crown to the head and continues to the tail with a mid-dorsal greyer section bordered by pure white flanks. Just like that of the skunk, the Ratel's distinctive colouration serves as a warning to other animals and man to avoid this odd and somewhat dangerous animal.

The Indian Grey Mongoose *(Herpestes edwardsi)* is as unexpected in Kuwait as the Honey Badger is spectacular and sightings are usually discounted. This species is, however, only known to occur in the Arabian peninsula at sea ports along the western and northern coast of the Gulf. It seems possible that it may have been introduced from the opposite shore and established itself in shoreline commerical and residential areas. In India it is abundant in and near villages and occasionally occurs in open country living under rocks and in

Common Red Fox *(Vulpes vulpes)*. An alert juvenile stands at the entrance to its earth. Without being able to see the ear tips and tail it is possible that this animal may be Ruppell's Sand Fox *(Vulpes ruppelli)* a close relative of the Common Red Fox (IW)

burrows. It is agile, inquisitive, diurnal and has a catholic diet that includes snakes and small animals, as well as carrion, fruit and roots. As is typical of the Viverridae, the Indian Grey Mongoose has short legs, a long body and a long barred tail. The coarse coat is a light orange-brown underneath and a speckled black and buffy-white dorsally.

In size and shape the Wild Cat *(Felis silvestris)* is like a large but slender domestic cat. It has a pale uniform sandy coat in which the typical tabby cat facial marking and body streaks are very faint. This felid is largely nocturnal and preys on small mammals and birds but will take insects, even darkling beetles, when food is scarce. It prefers rocky habitats and bushy shrub country but the presence of long hairs on its feet suggests that it may find its way into sandier regions.

The Caracal Lynx *(Caracal caracal)* cannot be mistaken for any other Arabian cat. It is a long-legged, medium-sized felid with a uniform reddish sand colour, long ear tufts and pronounced cheek ruffs. Its secretive manner and good camouflage make sightings of it scarce. It is mainly nocturnal but will hunt by day in cool or cloudy weather.

Honey Badger *(Mellivora capensis)*. Unfortunately killed during excavation work close to the north-western border of Kuwait, the skeleton of this distinctive animal is now in Kuwait Museum. Being nocturnal, the Ratel is rarely seen by man (MS)

The Arabic name 'Anaq al ardh' indicates its habit of dwelling in rock crevices and underground lairs. The caracal is even more agile than the mongoose, being able to leap as much as two metres to pluck a bird out of the air with its forepaws. According to one authority, its speed is greater than that of other cats of its size. Together with the Cheetah it was formerly trained in India for hunting small game. Its normal diet consists of birds and mammals up to the size of a small antelope.

The chapter began by considering some characteristic animals of deserts the world over and it seems appropriate to finish with one that, more than any other, typifies deserts of the Middle East. No account of the mammals of Kuwait would be complete without mentioning the Arabian Camel (*Camelus dromedarius*). For centuries the desert tribesmen's nomadic way of life has been inextricably linked to the Arabian Camel, an implicit acknowledgement of the exceptional physical and physiological adaptations of this animal to life in arid lands. Some adaptations allow the animal to cope with a sandy environment, whilst others help in water conservation and temperature control. The camel has long eyelashes that protect the eyes

Arabian Camel *(Camelus dromedarius)*. Grazing camels may actually help conserve desert vegetation. They graze over wide areas and, irrespective of the quality of vegetation, only take a few bites from each plant thereby stimulating further growth. Sheep and goats, however, totally denude plants of any green shoots (CWTP)

Arabian Camel *(Camelus dromedarius)* and Dog *(Canis familiaris)*. Beautifully adapted to its way, of life in the desert, the camel has played a central role in man's colonisation of the desert regions of the world (WAS)

from wind-blown sand and muscular nostrils that can be closed. Its two-toed feet have large fleshy pads that minimise sinking into soft sand. The thick, well ventilated, woollen coat acts as a barrier to solar radiation, but at the same time allows sweating to occur on the skin where it will be most effective in reducing the animal's temperature. The camel's hump is a mobile food reserve consisting of a localised accumulation of the animal's body fat. The hump does not hold water as was originally suspected, nor does the fat it contains act as a 'metabolic water store' as was subsequently thought. This misconception arose because of the fact that, in comparison with equivalent amounts of other energy sources such as carbohydrates and proteins, fat produces more water when it is broken down during metabolism. The extra oxygen that must be used to oxidise the fat, however, involves extra loss of water through the lungs, which just about cancels out any gains from the oxidation of the fat. What is odd about the hump is not that it is a food store, but that the store is a hump on the camel's back. Many different mammals accumulate fat as a reserve food supply but it is usually distributed evenly over the body. Because fat is such a good insulator, how-

Domestic Sheep *(Ovis aries)* and Domestic Goats *(Capra hircus)*. Flocks of these animals serve as a source of meat, fine leather and, more importantly, milk for their Bedouin owners (CWTP)

ever, mammals that live in hot climates concentrate the fat in one deposit so that the rest of the body surface can act as a radiator. In camels the large deposit lies in the hump as is true of Indian and Zebu cattle, whilst in desert sheep the fat store is in the tail.

The camel has a remarkable capacity to withstand drought and in the summer may exist on dry food alone for as much as two weeks. It achieves this through the combination of an ability to withstand a high degree of water depletion without losing its appetite and an unusually large drinking capacity. A camel can easily tolerate the loss of water equal to a quarter of its body weight, whereas a man losing an eighth of his body water would be in serious trouble. In Man, the water is lost from the blood, which becomes viscous and difficult to circulate. This puts a strain on the heart that steadily increases until about a fifth of the body water has been lost. The blood is then unable to circulate sufficiently well to carry away metabolic heat to the skin and body temperature rises quickly resulting in 'explosive heat death'. The camel avoids this by maintaining the blood volume at the expense of the water in the tissues. After severe dehydration camels have been known to drink over one hundred litres in less than ten minutes, turning from emaciated skeletons with protruding ribs back to their normal healthy condition. Within two days the water is evenly distributed over the whole body, diluting blood and tissue fluids to an extent intolerable to other mammals which would have died of water intoxication at a much lower water intake.

In the majority of mammals, including Man, most water is lost through sweating to maintain a constant body temperature. The camel, however, allows its body temperature to increase by about 6° C during the course of the day, saving the water it would have used to maintain the lower temperature. When the ambient temperature drops at night the stored heat is simply lost without the need to use water in evaporative cooling. Unlike the Arabian Oryx *(Oryx leucoryx)*, the camel cannot be totally independent of drinking water but is able to economise on its use and can also tolerate great variation in water content and body temperature. Nevertheless it is an amazing beast well worthy of the central role it has played in Man's colonisation of desert regions throughout the world.

Opposite: **Arabian Camel** *(Camelus dromadarius)*. Morphologically as well as physiologically, the camel is well adapted to life in a desert. Thick long eyelashes protect the eyes and in the severest sand storm the eyelids are transluscent enough to enable the camel to continue walking with its eyes shut (ANHG)

Marine Life

By
Tony Farmer

The Arabian Gulf is part of the Indo-Pacific Region, which, in terms of the number of plant and animal species, is the richest on Earth. The nearest equivalent is the tropical rain forests of South America. Unfortunately, much of the remarkable marine life for which the Indo-Pacific is noted is not found in the waters of Kuwait. There are a number of reasons for this which are associated with both the geographical position of Kuwait itself and the general environmental characteristics of the Gulf as a whole.

Most obviously, the Gulf is surrounded by large land masses creating, in essence, a small version of the Mediterranean Sea. This means that the Gulf coastline has a continental climate with extremes of temperature. The rest of the Indo-Pacific Region has a more equable tropical or sub-tropical climate because of the stabilising influence of the heat that is stored in the adjacent water mass. The relatively small and shallow Gulf stores little heat and its temperature ranges from 12 °C to 36 °C throughout the year.

Khiran. Seen here from the air, Khor Al-Mufateh and Khor Al-A'ma are the only two inlets along the coastline. Tidal at their entrances, salinity rapidly increases as one moves inland producing a unique environment with its own specialised fauna (ASDF)

195

Southern shores. Cold onshore winds whip up the high spring tides of winter to produce rough seas more typical of the Atlantic than the Gulf (JNBB)

High air temperatures coupled with low relative humidities result in exceptionally high evaporation rates and since rainfall and water run-off from the land are limited within the area, a net loss of water from the Gulf leads to increased salinities. Salinity, a measure of the quantity of all salts present in seawater, normally ranges between 3.4 and 3.6 % in the world's oceans, whereas that in the Gulf generally lies between 3.8 and 4.2 %. In coastal lagoons and land-locked shallow bodies of water salinities may rise to 18 % or more.

Although temperature and salinity are the most important factors affecting the Gulf's marine life, they are not the only ones. Water circulation affects the availability and distribution of nutrients and water-borne sediments, particularly those from river systems and their estuaries. Tidal range influences the number and type of species found on the seashore and, further out in deeper water, light intensity is important.

The interaction of these factors and the environment they create is responsible not only for the distribution of individual species but also for the presence of whole communities of plants and animals. Kuwait is fortunate in this respect compared with other regions lower down the Gulf. Situated at the head of the Gulf adjacent to the only major source of fresh water, Kuwait exhibits a range of salinity, sediments and tidal regimes as one moves from north to south. Thus, the communities that are found are more varied than they might otherwise be.

Water movement around Kuwait is generally dependent on the anticlockwise circulation in the northern Arabian Gulf. The fresh water from the Shatt Al-Arab estuary flows southwards past Kuwait to Saudi Arabia, bringing large amounts of fine suspended material and causing the northern part of Kuwait waters to be generally less saline than the south. In addition, there are large areas of mud and clay both intertidally and offshore in northern Kuwait waters, and islands such as Warba and Bubiyan have developed as a part of the growth of the Shatt Al-Arab delta. Elsewhere sediments may consist of sand, shell gravel or rock.

Rocky shore. The dhow building yards along the rocky shoreline of the Dohah peninsula are a reminder that sea-faring and boat building were among the most important economic activities of earlier times (TCV)

Tidal ranges vary from about 1 m in the extreme south of Kuwait to between 3 and 4 m at the northern end of Khor As-Subiyah adjacent to Warba island. The intertidal fauna and flora are greatly affected by the tidal range, and there is a definite succession of species and communities related to the length of time that a particular level of beach is exposed. Zonation may not be as obvious as in temperate waters because of the absence of large species of seaweeds or macrophytes.

To describe the commonest and the most interesting marine species found in Kuwait waters, the following area will be dealt with separately: northern parts of Kuwait's coastline, waters, and the areas around Failaka, Bubiyan and Warba; central and southern shores of Kuwait to the east and south of Shuwaikh port to the Saudi Arabian border; offshore areas including Kuwait's commercial fishing grounds; coral reefs primarily in the vicinity of Kubbar, Qaruh and Um Al-Maradim islands; ephemeral pools and the creeks at Khiran.

Very little scientific study has been carried out on the marine flora and fauna of Kuwait and it should therefore be noted that some of the identifications given are provisional. Increased interest in the local marine life will help this situation, although it will be some years before most species can be positively identified.

Ocypode crab *(Cleistostoma kuwaitensis)*. Found only on the high shore at approximately the same level as the fiddler crabs, this deposit feeding crab has, until recently, been undescribed. Future study will undoubtedly reveal yet other new species in these rich mudflats (DAC)

Northern Shores

The northern part of Kuwait's coastline is characterised by extensive tidal mudflats which are formed from the settling of fine particles coming from the Shatt Al-Arab. These mudflats are extremely level and very large areas are uncovered at low tide; on the northern side of Kuwait Bay several kilometres may be exposed between high and low water. In a few places there are rocky outcrops, but generally the expanse of mud is unbroken and offshore the sediments are essentially of similar origin and type. Tidal mudflats are known to be one of the most productive marine ecosystems in the world. In the case of Kuwait Bay, the less saline water from the Shatt Al-Arab provides a source of nutrients and organic matter that is essential for supporting the large numbers of organisms present. Under the thin surface layer of mud, which is well oxygenated, the sediment is often black and evil-smelling due to

Sulaibikhat Bay. The northern part of Kuwait's coastline is characterised by extensive tidal mudflats. The most sheltered mudflats with the best developed fauna are those of Kadmah and Sulaibikhat (GWW)

hydrogen sulphide gas formed by bacteria that do not need oxygen. The habitat is a source of food for members of the terrestrial and marine fauna. Because of their productivity, the tidal mudflats represent a very important source of food for wading birds at low tide and various species of fish at high tide.

Because of the low relief of the mudflats, the marine and terrestrial environments or zones tend to blend imperceptibly into each other, especially as the upper tidal limit may vary considerably throughout the year as a result of small changes in tide levels. The highest part of the mudflats supports large numbers of salt-tolerant plants or halophytes, which are able to withstand high salt concentrations and occasional immersion such as occurs particularly during spring tides. These species have already been mentioned in the chapter on Vegetation. In sheltered areas below the halophyte zone there is often an expanse of algal mats which survive long periods of exposure during each tidal cycle. These algal mats are composed primarily of blue-green algae (genus *Chroococcus*) and diatoms. A wide variety of invertebrates that may include marine worms (Polychaeta and Nematoda), marine snails (Gastropoda) and some burrowing crabs live amongst them. Algal mats, however, do not carry the same wealth of animal life that is found in the next slightly lower zone, which is dominated by a number of species of mudskipper and burrowing crabs of the genera *Macrophthalmus, Eurycarcinus* and *Cleistostoma.*

Opposite: **Sunrise over Sulaibikhat Bay.** Local tidal conditions act to ameliorate the harsh climatic conditions imposed upon intertidal organisms, as longest periods of exposure coincide with the highest daily air temperatures in winter and with the lowest in summer (DAC)

Grey Heron *(Ardea cinerea)*. Mudflats represent a very important source of food for a wide variety of animals including many birds. During winter, terns, gulls and herons find easy prey among the relatively sluggish Mudskippers (WAS)

The most obvious of the fish using the rich mud-flat habitat are three species of amphibious mud-skippers, which can be seen scuttling about on the upper reaches of the exposed mud at low tide. Apart from living in burrows excavated in the mud, the different types of mudskipper have little in common. *Periophthalmus koelreuteri* is a carnivore and can be seen stalking and lunging at small crabs that are its main diet. As the most amphibious of the three fish, *P. koelreuteri* spends almost all of its time out of water. The largest mudskipper, *Boleophthalmus boddarti,* is a herbivore and can be seen feeding by side-to-side head movements on the diatoms and algae found on the mud surface. This species is less active and is usually seen lying in a pool of water with just its head and eyes protruding. Resembling an emaciated *Boleophthalmus* with bulbous eyes, the

Xanthid crab *(Eurycarcinus orientalis.)* A white burrowing crab, often with purple tips to its claws, which lives in large numbers in soft or sandy mud at around high water mark. The burrows are 2-3 cm in diameter and usually nearly horizontal (DAC)

Mudskipper *(Periophthalmus koelreuteri)*. This species of fish is a goby but is amphibious. It may be found in large numbers but is confined to a narrow coastal strip at the edge of the mudflats (CWTP)

third mudskipper, *Scartelaos viridis,* is almost entirely confined to the standing water left after the tide recedes. This fish is an omnivore, biting into the mud to obtain the minute animals and plants that live just below the surface.

Chasing, leaping and fin-erection are all part of the mudskippers' fighting and courtship, but the building behaviour of the carnivorous *P. koel-reuteri,* and particularly that of the herbivorous *B. boddarti,* is especially interesting. Both excavate their burrows by carrying mouthfuls of mud to the surface. The carnivore uses this mud to construct turrets or large saucer-shaped entrances to its burrow whilst the herbivore builds and maintains unique, extensive mud-walled polygonal territories. Even though these fish are found elsewhere in Kuwait and throughout the Indo-Pacific Region, the construction of territories is confined to Sulaibikhat Bay. It is almost certain that this Kuwait population represents the only example of this unusual form of animal architecture in the world.

Mudskipper *(Boleophthalmus boddarti)*. This is the largest of Kuwait's three species and is herbivorous. The species is unique in constructing polygonal territories with mud-walled boundaries (CWTP)

Polygonal territories of the mudskipper *(B. boddarti)* which retain water at
low tide. Generally the burrow entrance is at the centre of each territory.
The mudskippers spend most of their time feeding on minute plants on the
surface of the mud or maintaining the boundary walls (DAC)

Mudskipper and crab *(Scartelaos viridis* and *Macrophthalmus pectinipes)*. This mudskipper is easily identified by the filamentous dorsal fin
which is erected during movement. The least amphibious mudskipper, it is
confined to the *Macrophthalmus* zone where water remains on the surface
at low tide (DAC)

In isolated areas, particularly where the mudflats are slightly better drained at low water, large numbers of rival male fiddler crabs *(Uca* sp.) may be seen waving their large white claws in threat displays. Like the fiddler crabs, *Macrophthalmus pectinipes* has long eyestalks but is usually blue. Most of the burrowing crabs are deposit feeders, either ingesting the thin surface layer of the mud or working it with their mouthparts to remove the edible organic matter.

The small but heavily built white crab *Eurycarcinus orientalis* is, however, a carnivore preying on smaller crabs and fish. It is also to be found at the lowest zone of the shore above extreme low water mark. Here the dominant organism is usually the small Banded Horn Shell, *Cerithidea cingulata,* and up to 2-3000 per square metre can be found. This zone also contains a number of burrowing bivalves that likewise ingest the organic particles within the thin upper layer of the sediment.

Fiddler crab *(Uca annulipes)*. Dense populations of fiddler crabs may be found in isolated patches along Kuwait's northern shores. The males have one greatly enlarged claw, which they wave like a fiddler's bow, whilst both claws of the females are small (ASDF)

205

Banded Horn Shell *(Cerithidea cingulata)*. Enormous numbers of these snails live on sheltered muddy beaches and feed on the microscopic plants and organic particles within the surface layer of the mudflats (ASDF)

Ocypode crab. *(Macrophthalmus pectinipes)*. The largest and most conspicuous of the intertidal mudflat crabs, *M. pectinipes,* occur in a zone overlapping that of the mudskippers and extending as far down as the low water mark (DAC)

Ocypode crab *(Macrophthalmus depressus)*. There is a great variety of mudflat crabs, each adapted to specific environmental conditions. This species is found along the coast wherever sandy mud occurs and on mudflats replaces *M. pectinipes* which prefers a pure mud habitat (DAJ)

Algal mat polygonal zone. The salinity gradient across the mat and the alternate wetting and drying of it produces changes in surface morphology. Cinder, polygonal, crinkle and flat zones are descriptive of the surface appearance of the crust as one moves away from the sea (DAC)

Algal mat crinkle zone. The upper reaches of the intertidal zone are often marked by a band of laminated algal mats. They are characterized by layers of intertwined filamentous and unicellular blue-green algae which bind and trap sediment that is washed onto them (DAC)

A few animals can survive the lack of oxygen below the surface but the majority need to pump water from the surface above. By burrowing, these animals help to bring sediment to the surface where, under the influence of the oxygen in the air, it changes colour, loses its hydrogen sulphide and adds to the community's food supply.

Organisms not normally associated with mudflats may be found attached to isolated patches of loose rock or shell. These include a rock oyster (*Saccostrea cucullata*), a pearl oyster (*Pinctada margaritifera*) and numerous tube-building polychaete worms.

The zones and the species within them may vary considerably in different parts of the mudflat. Such variations are usually related to topography, sediment particle size or other factors connected with temperature and salinity. Topography can have an effect by altering the length of time an animal is exposed and can also influence the drainage of surface water from burrows or from sediment particles. It should be remembered that animals living between the tide marks are exposed not only to desiccation when the water recedes but also to high temperatures. This is why many of the animals remain in their burrows except for short feeding periods or when in search of mates.

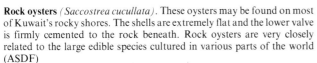

Rock oysters (*Saccostrea cucullata*). These oysters may be found on most of Kuwait's rocky shores. The shells are extremely flat and the lower valve is firmly cemented to the rock beneath. Rock oysters are very closely related to the large edible species cultured in various parts of the world (ASDF)

Intertidal marine plants are conspicuous by their absence and are replaced by the microscopic plants or phytoplankton in the inshore waters. It is interesting to note that in the more southern regions of the Arabian Gulf the tidal mudflats have a well-developed zone of Dwarf Mangroves (*Avicennia marina*), but no mudskippers between the level of the algal mats and the *Macrophthalmus* crabs. The mangrove zone is totally absent in Kuwait, probably because of the lower winter temperatures.

Polychaete worms (Serpulidae). Vast numbers of tube-building worms occur on most of the northern beaches growing on almost every available hard surface including rocks, rubble, old shells, rubbish, pipes and jetties. They feed by filtering minute organisms and organic particles from the water (ASDF)

Southern Shores

The central and southern shores of Kuwait are predominantly composed of sand, although in isolated areas there may be outcrops of cap rock between the tides or miniature limestone cliffs at the top of the beach. As one moves south from Shuwaikh port, the proportion of mud in the beach deposits progressively decreases until most of the southern beaches are of clean fine-grained sand. Much of this sand originates from the desert, although there is often an admixture of shell gravel. Usually the sand on exposed beaches is coarser than that of sheltered ones. Zonation on sandy beaches is either non-existent or not obvious because the animals are hidden from view and their burrow entrances do not remain open.

Ghost crab *(Ocypode saratan)*. Ghost crabs live in small numbers above high water mark along most of Kuwait's southern shores. They are extremely aggressive and may tackle prey much larger than themselves. Although normally predatory they also eat carrion. The eyes are large and carried on long stalks, giving the crab excellent all-round vision (WAS)

Burrow and mound of a ghost crab *(Ocypode saratan)*. During the construction of their burrows, male ghost crabs deposit the excavated sand in a heap which is used a territory marker. If not disturbed the males may be seen standing on the tops or sides of these mounds looking for rivals or mates (ASDF)

One of the most conspicuous animals on Kuwait's sandy beaches is the ghost crab *(Ocypode saratan)*, the males of which build conical sand towers 20-30 cm high next to their burrow entrances above high water mark. These towers act as territorial signals to members of the same species. This crab is unusual in that it is virtually terrestrial in its habits although its larvae are planktonic like those of all other crabs. The ghost crab eats smaller animals and carrion, but is very aggressive and may attack and kill animals of its own size or larger, such as young turtles.

On many sandy beaches the highest zone is marked by enormous numbers of small balls of sand lying outside the mouths of tiny burrows. These balls result from the activities of the crab *Scopimera scabricauda,* which, like its mud-dwelling counterpart, picks up sand from the surface and eats the micro-organisms growing on the surface of the sand grains. If the sand is not well drained or is slightly muddy, the place of *S. scabricauda* is taken by another crab, *Ilyoplax* sp., which is also less than 1 cm across the body. At

Sea squirt (Tunicata). The majority of sea squirts are sessile bottom-dwelling animals that feed on plankton filtered from the sea. Although these were found in the rocky intertidal area, sea squirts are also common in similar subtidal habitats (KR)

Rocky areas have a fauna and flora of their own. With the exception of seagrasses, which have true roots to anchor them to the seabed, most marine plants or seaweeds require a hard substrate for attachment. Unlike the rocky shores of temperate or arctic regions which have a distinctive cover of seaweeds, most tropical and subtropical beaches are almost totally devoid of them. This is because desiccation during periods of exposure to high air and surface temperatures eliminates virtually all species. Only in rockpools, under overhangs or ledges, or where there is water run-off across the beach are algae to be found.

Seaslaters such as *Ligia* sp. and *Petrobius* sp. (wingless insects related to the domestic silverfish) live on rocky beaches at approximately the level of the highest tides. On the upper surfaces of rocks between the tides, the tubes of worms of the

Sea snake *(Pelamis platurus)*. One method this snake uses to catch its prey is to lie motionless on the surface of the water to attract small fish. When several have gathered a sudden lunge by the snake easily secures its victim. Occasionally, as here, sea snakes are found on the beach. Since they are extremely venomous they should not be handled (KR)

Bryozoan *(Membranipora* sp.*)*. Bryozoans are abundant, but inconspicuous, colonial animals that encrust hard surfaces in the marine environment. This one is on rock in the intertidal region (KR)

Family Serpulidae may be extremely abundant and cover virtually every available surface. Acorn barnacles *(Balanus* sp.*)* and small oysters *(Saccostrea* sp.*)* may also occur in moderately large numbers where the silt content of the water is reduced. On the sides and undersides of stones one may find a multitude of molluscs and crustaceans and, burrowing between the rocks and living in the crevices, a wide range of polychaete worms. The minute ribbed mussel *(Brachidontes* sp.*)* may be extremely numerous, whereas the date mussels *(Lithophaga* sp.*)*, although widespread, usually

Feather-duster or fan worm (Sabellidae). As illustrated by this Red Sea specimen, many polychaete worms are brilliantly coloured. The large fan surrounding the mouth is used to filter food particles from the sea. When danger threatens the whole animal including the fan retracts into the tube in which the animal lives (NRA)

Sea pens (Pennatulacea). Sea pens are fleshy colonial animals related to corals but having more in common with sea fans and whip corals. Often brightly coloured, these eight-tentacled animals feed on plankton (KR).

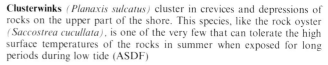

Clusterwinks *(Planaxis sulcatus)* cluster in crevices and depressions of rocks on the upper part of the shore. This species, like the rock oyster *(Saccostrea cucullata)*, is one of the very few that can tolerate the high surface temperatures of the rocks in summer when exposed for long periods during low tide (ASDF)

occur singly. Also common intertidally are numerous marine snails and a pulmonate slug *(Onchidium verruculatum)* which, by virtue of its mottled and granular skin, is beautifully camouflaged whether it is living on the surface of rocks or on muddy sand. The commonest shore crab is *Metapograpsus messor* which scuttles about over the rocks looking for food. Porcelain crabs (genus *Petrolisthes*) and the pistol shrimps (genera *Alpheus* and *Synalpheus*), which make the characteristic cracking noise with their highly specialised claws, are common under rocks and stones. Occasionally a specimen of the mantis shrimp *(Lysiosquilla* sp.) may be found, lying in wait to grab passing prey with its raptorial first pair of legs.

Acorn barnacles *(Balanus sp.)*. Barnacles are not at all common on Kuwait's beaches, although they may be found in small numbers nestling among masses of tube worms attached to rock and other stable surfaces. However, they are often responsible for the fouling of the bottoms of boats and ships (ASDF)

Sea slug *(Onchidium verruculatum)*. A trail of faeces indicates the direction of travel in this slow-moving animal. At low tide these sea slugs emerge from their shelter and slowly wander over the rocks eating the algae that grow there. As they move they lay trails and so are able to find their way back to the same shelter after each foraging trip (IDM)

Sea slug *(Onchidium verruculatum)*. This animal is a fairly common inhabitant of the intertidal zone of both rocky and muddy shores. The cryptic colouration and warty skin provide excellent camouflage. This particular species is air-breathing and has a lung rather than gills (ASDF)

Porcelain crab *(Petrolisthes lamarckii)*. This is another common crab, but one that is seldom seen unless one looks under rocks and in crevices. The porcelain crabs are not true crabs but are closely related to the hermit crabs and squat lobsters *(ASDF)*

Shore crab *(Metapograpsus messor)*. This is surely Kuwait's most conspicuous and commonest shore crab. Large numbers may be seen scampering over rocks and debris along most of Kuwait's central and southern shores (ASDF)

Cushion-star *(Asterina cephea)*. Cushion stars may be found under loose rocks and stones along most of the coast. These small starfish feed on small animals living on the underside of rocks, by everting their stomachs and engulfing the prey (ASDF)

At extremely low levels small colonies of coral may be found, but these occur in isolated patches. Deep purple sea-urchins are sometimes plentiful in cracks and crevices at the lowest tidal levels and their distribution extends into deeper water. Those with short spines are mostly *Echinometra mathaei.* Armed with extremely long and fragile spines, *Diadema setosum* should be treated with respect as the sharp spines may cause extremely painful injuries.

Sea cucumber (Holothuridae). There are several species of these echinoderms in Kuwait. They are common under rocks and on the sand bars in rocky shores and feed on plankton and detritus (KR)

Sea-urchin *(Diadema setosum)*. This species belongs to a group of sea-urchins which generally live on coral reefs or among rocks and are characterised by their extremely long sharp spines. The spines are very fragile and can inflict painful injuries if the animal is handled (ASDF)

Of those plant species likely to be found on rocky shores, limited areas of *Sargassum* sp. and *Dictyota* sp. may occur in rock pools. At extreme low tides carpets of *Acetabularia,* which looks like a miniature parasol about 0.5-1.0 cm high, may be found.

Brittlestar (Ophiuroidea). Active at night, brittlestars remain buried in the sediment or hidden beneath stones or seaweed during the day. As the English name implies, the arms are easily cast off, but, like those of the starfish, can be regenerated (GR)

Offshore

In the offshore areas the species of most immediate interest are the fish and shrimps that support Kuwait's commercial fisheries. There are about a dozen species of penaeid shrimps occurring in Kuwait waters of which three species are important: *Penaeus semisulcatus, Metapenaeus affinis* and *Parapenaeopsis stylifera.* The first is distributed throughout the area and supports the industrial export fishery, while the two smaller species are found in northern Kuwait waters and are landed by dhows at the Sief Palace fishing port. All these species are found on sand and muddy-sand bottoms.

Opposite: **Pencil urchin** *(Cidaris* sp.*)*. With their heavy blunt-tipped spines these sea urchins can be found wedged against rocks in shallow subtidal or intertidal areas. The urchin obtains its food by scraping it off the ground (KR)

Shrimp *(Penaeus semisulcatus)*. Of the dozen or so species of penaeid shrimp that occur in the Arabian Gulf this is the largest and the most important commercially. Most of the landings of this species are exported from Kuwait (ASDF)

Shrimp *(Metapenaeus affinis)*. The local dhow fishery is largely dependent on this slightly smaller species of shrimp. The green colouration is due to the underlying ovary showing through the shell (ASDF)

Sharks (Carcharhinidae). During summer months large numbers of sharks, 2-4 m in length, appear in Kuwait waters. These are normally found only offshore and often appear in large numbers to feed on trash fish discarded by trawlers (ASDF)

In the same fishing grounds many commercially important fish species may be caught. These include the Hamoor *(Epinephelus tauvina)*, Sheim *(Acanthopagrus latus)*, Sobaity *(Acanthopagrus cuvieri)*, Nakroor *(Pomadasys argenteus)* and Zobaidy *(Pampus argenteus)*.

Many of the fish caught by the commercial trawlers are elasmobranchs or cartilaginous fishes. These are the sharks, rays, sawfish and guitarfish. Sharks can range in size from the small cat shark, *Chiloscyllium griseus,* which grows to about 1 m in length, to large Carcharhinidae (Requiem sharks) of 3 to 4 m. Many of the so-called black-tipped sharks are difficult to identify. Generally the large sharks are absent from Kuwait waters during the winter, but may be quite common in summer. In July and August it is not unusual to see a hundred or more sharks following a fishing boat waiting for the trash fish and offal to be thrown overboard. Although there are stories of fishermen, and pearl divers in particular, being attacked by sharks, there appear to be no documented reports in recent years. The presence of sharks in Kuwait waters should not deter bathing, although care should be taken whilst diving or fishing offshore.

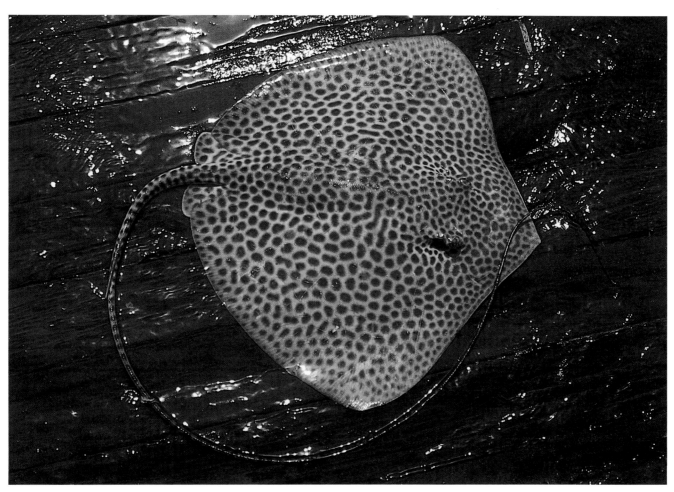

Spotted stingray *(Himantura uarnak)*. Stingrays are common on the fishing grounds, although they may occasionally be seen in shallow water at low tide. Near the end of the tail they have one or more poisonous barbed spines used for defence (ASDF)

Spotted stingray *(H. uarnak)* giving birth to its young. Two small rays have already been born whilst the third is being expelled from the cloaca of the female (ASDF)

In early summer the sawfish (genus *Pristis*) also arrive in Kuwait waters, presumably from the Indian Ocean. One of the largest species of fish in the world, the Whale Shark *(Rhincodon typus)* has been recorded in the Gulf on a number of occasions, although its appearance in Kuwait waters is a rare event. Rays and guitarfish have become adapted to a bottom-living existence. There is a relatively large number of species of rays in Kuwait waters, some of which should be handled carefully as the stinging spines in the tail can inflict painful wounds that take a long time to heal. The largest of the rays likely to be encountered in Kuwait waters is the devil ray *Mobula diabolus*, which may have a wingspan of up to 2 m. These fish have a habit of jumping out of the water and returning with a resounding crash.

The bony fish or teleosts comprise the vast majority of fish species, even though the cartilaginous ones may sometimes outnumber them in the catches of the shrimp boats. Many of the surface-living or pelagic bony fish such as anchovies and sardines (Engraulidae and Clupeidae) feed exclusively on plankton. Other pelagic species, in particular the jacks and mackerels (Carangidae and Scombridae), may be predatory. It is thought that there are more than two hundred species of teleosts in Kuwait waters, and they occur in an almost bewildering variety of shapes, from sea-horses *(Hippocampus* sp.*)* to a sailfish *(Istiophorus gladius),* which is much sought after by sport fishermen. Some species swimming near the surface such as Hakool *(Ablennes hians)* and Sils *(Hemiramphus marginatus)* are extremely long and thin and have one or both jaws elongated for catching small fish at speed. When startled, these small fish may take to the air in a series of jumps in order to outrun and confuse the predator.

Five-lined Cardinalfish *(Cheilodipterus quinquelineatus).* These cardinal-fish occur in large schools around coral reefs and rock ledges and are one of the most conspicious coral reef inhabitants (RW)

Siny *(Leiognathus fasciatus).* This is one of the commonest species of fish caught by the shrimp trawlers. They normally occur in large shoals and although good to eat are normally discarded at sea because of their small size (ASDF)

Lionfish *(Pterois* sp.*)*. This is another poisonous species which generally lives amongst coral reefs. Although difficult to catch and handle they make excellent subjects for marine aquaria (NRA)

Flyingfish are quite common in Kuwait waters and can be seen, especially on summer evenings, jumping from the bow waves of small boats and sailing away just above the surface of the water for up to 100 m. The enlarged lower lobe of the tail is used to scull the fish along so that it can gain speed rapidly and therefore become completely airborne.

Some of the teleosts such as the Crimson Snapper *(Lutjanus coccineus)*, the Yellow-marked Angelfish *(Pomacanthus maculosus)* and the poisonous Striped Catfish, *Plotosus anguillaris,* are brilliantly coloured. Of the brightly coloured fish living in the

223

Butterflyfish *(Chaetodon malapterus)*. This is a predominantly reef-living species. Butterflyfish include some of the most beautiful and brilliantly coloured marine fish. They feed on small invertebrates among the coral heads and on the coral themselves (RW)

Stonefish *(Leptosynanceja melanostigma)*. Stonefish can be found in shallow water at low tide along most of Kuwait's muddy and sandy shores. The brilliant orange pectoral fins are normally hidden, but may be 'flashed' at would-be predators to warn them of the poisonous spines (CWTP)

coral reefs, some rely on their distinctive patterns and vivid colours to identify members of the same species, whereas others may exhibit warning colouration associated with being venomous. Although not associated with corals the stonefish, *Leptosynanceja melanostigma,* is a good example. Normally well camouflaged in order to catch its prey, it has bright orange pectoral fins that serve as a warning to would-be predators.

On the seabed there are teleosts that have evolved in a flattened form by lying on one side, unlike the rays, which are flattened dorso-ventrally. Depending on the species, either side can have become the upper pigmented surface whilst the lower surface, like the underside of most fish, is pale. The eye from the lower surface has migrated to the upper, giving the head a distorted appearance. Some species of flatfish such as the Zebra Sole *(Aesopia cornuta)* and the Spotted Sole *(Pardachirus marmoratus),* which has a peculiar hieroglyph pattern on its back, are beautifully coloured. The tongue soles such as *Cynoglossus macrolepidotus* are extremely numerous on muddy and muddy-sand bottoms.

Heart-urchin *(Metalia persica)*. Heart-urchins are sometimes caught in enormous numbers by shrimp fisherman. Although they are burrowing animals, they are dug out of the mud by the heavy foot-rope of the shrimp trawl (ASDF)

Cuttlefish *(Sepia sp.)*. During the summer months large numbers of cuttlefish, often in pairs, come inshore to mate and lay eggs and can be observed easily with the aid of a face mask and snorkel (RW)

Spotted Sole *(Pardachirus marmoratus)*. This unusual species is one of the most beautiful of the flat fish. The significance of the orange hieroglyph on its side is not known although it has been suggested that it might be a warning pattern (ASDF)

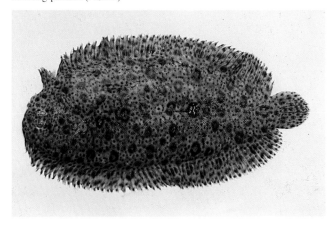

Cephalopods are also part of the fauna of open waters, and cuttlefish *(Sepia* sp.) and squids may occur in sizeable shoals. During the summer large numbers of cuttlefish come inshore to mate and to lay eggs and couples can be seen in the summer lazily swimming after each other over the sand and rocks just off Kuwait's southern beaches. Their large globular eggs (1 cm diameter) are normally attached in clumps to rocks or weed, but are often washed up on the beach. The development of the

Eggs of the cuttlefish *(Sepia officinalis)*. Large numbers of cuttlefish eggs are sometimes washed up after storms. Normally they are attached to rocks and seaweed until the young cuttlefish have developed fully and are ready to hatch (MD)

Opposite: **Bottle-nosed Dolphin** *(Tursiops aduncus)*. This animal is just about to dive after taking a breath of air at the surface. The dorsal blow hole (nostril) can be clearly seen (ASDF)

young cuttlefish may be followed through the transparent membrane of the egg and, just prior to hatching, a perfect miniature replica of the adult cuttlefish swims about inside the egg. It can even jettison ink from its ink sac whilst still in the egg, so that immediately after hatching it can take advantage of this escape mechanism used by most of the cephalopods.

Dolphins or porpoises (there is no strict scientific distinction between these names) may be seen in the vicinity of the major ports in Kuwait and often follow vessels for considerable distances. The commonest dolphin is probably *Tursiops aduncus*, which is closely related to the Atlantic Bottle-nosed Dolphin. An unusual species recorded from Kuwait is the Black Finless Porpoise

(Neophocaena phocaenoides), which can be recognised by its small size, dark colour and absence of a dorsal fin. Occasionally whales have also been reported from Kuwait waters and the skeleton of a locally stranded Blue Whale *(Balaenoptera musculus)* can be seen in the Kuwait Science Museum.

With the exception of the predators, all fish are directly dependent on either planktonic or benthic (bottom living) organisms as their food source. Plankton is rich in Kuwait waters due to nutrients brought down by the Shatt Al-Arab. It includes adult forms of various shapes and sizes from microscopic copepods to large jellyfish and also the larval stages of most marine animals. This phase in the life cycle allows the animals to take advantage of the enormous productivity of the phytoplankton which, through photosynthesis, manufactures organic matter for the entire community or ecosystem. Pelagic larval forms allow the young stages to disperse over large distances, helping to ensure that sufficient animals will survive to reach maturity and maintain the size of the population.

Opposite: **Bottle-nosed Dolphins** *(Tursiops aduncus)*. Dolphins are rarely seen inshore but commonly follow fishing boats in deeper waters. Sharks and dolphins often compete for the trash fish discarded by the shrimp trawlers (ASDF)

Black Finless Porpoise *(Neophocaena phocaenoides)*. Although this species ranges from the Cape of Good Hope to Japan it is unusual in that it often frequents estuaries and may on occasion be found in the freshwater reaches of river systems (MS)

For several reasons most of the benthic animals are rarely seen. They do not usually occur inter-tidally, are not washed up on the beaches and are seldom caught whilst fishing. Only a single rather important member of this community will be mentioned here: the pearl oyster *Pinctada margaritifera*. Offshore in the south of Kuwait there was a traditional pearl diving industry; although what were formerly extensive beds of pearl oysters have been largely fished out. Pearls are formed in the same way that the nacreous lining of the shell is produced by the mantle, except they are produced around a nucleus. This nucleus may be a sand grain or even a parasite which has entered the flesh of the oyster and caused irritation. Large numbers of oysters, some of which contain small pearls, may be found; but no longer are densely populated pearl banks reported by pearl divers. Small specimens of the pearl oyster may be found at the lower levels of rocky beaches, although under these conditions they rarely contain pearls.

Plankton. A single drop of plankton filtered from the sea contains an enormous range of microscopic marine life. Whilst some species (e.g. copepods) complete their entire life cycle in the surface waters many others (e.g. shrimp and crabs) are only found in the plankton during their larval stages (ASDF)

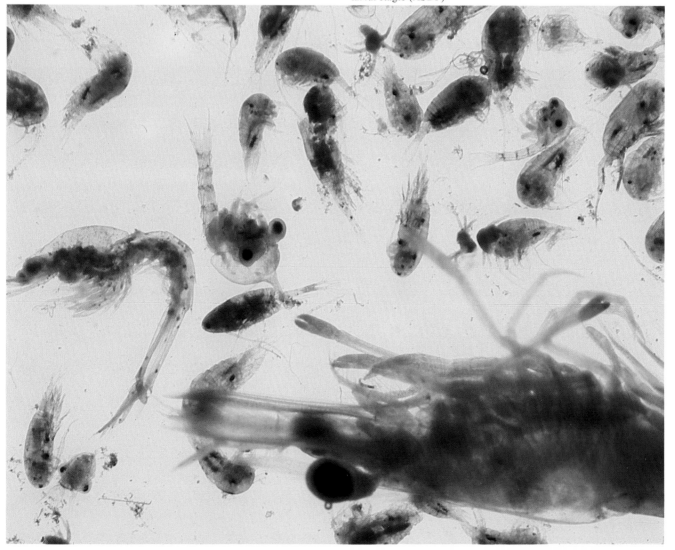

Brain coral *(Platygyra* sp.*)*. Although the detailed structure of a particular species of coral will remain the same, the overall shape is variable. Other plates show some of the different shapes that can be adopted by this brain coral (RW)

Coral Reefs

Coral reefs and isolated coral heads are not widespread in Kuwait waters because most reef-building corals cannot survive the low winter temperatures. Moreover, most species are unable to remove the large quantities of water-borne sediments from their surfaces and soon become smothered. Light-penetration is another important factor in determining the growth of coral since the polyps contain photosynthetic algal cells. Therefore coral growth is usually limited to depths of less than 15 m. Apart from a few isolated species that may be found at extreme low tides and occasionally offshore, most corals are found only in the south of Kuwait. There are small reefs around the offshore islands of Kubbar, Qaruh and Umm Al-Maradim. The waters in the vicinity of Kuwait's northern islands are much too silty to allow the development of any coral reefs.

Composed almost entirely of calcium carbonate coral is, of course, white when dead. Underwater most live corals appear as dull shades of grey, green or purple, but under suitable lighting some species exhibit deep red or bright orange coloration.

Basically there are four forms of coral growth: ramose or branching, foliose, encrusting and massive. Branching corals include the stag's horn corals of the genus *Acropora,* of which there are several species of a similar form. The foliose corals tend to be found in deeper water outside the reef platform and can take a wide variety of shapes. Encrusting corals may grow over rocks or the dead coral of other species. They may also grow over broken coral fragments on the seabed, cementing them together and therefore adding to the development of the whole reef structure. The aptly named brain corals, such as *Platygyra* sp., have rounded heads covered with convoluted furrows and produce the main structure of most coral reefs.

Opposite: **Umm Al-Maradim.** The majority of coral reefs in the Gulf are platform reefs but those of the Kuwait islands are fringing reefs. Seen from the air, the fringing reef of Umm Al-Maradim is a good example, with the coral forming a more or less continuous border close to the shore of the island (ND)

Coral reef *(Porites* sp.*)*. One reason for the abundance of marine life on a coral reef is that it provides many crevices and crannies in which other animals can hide. Many of the same animals also utilise other 'refuging reefs' such as sunken ships and oil platform supports (RW)

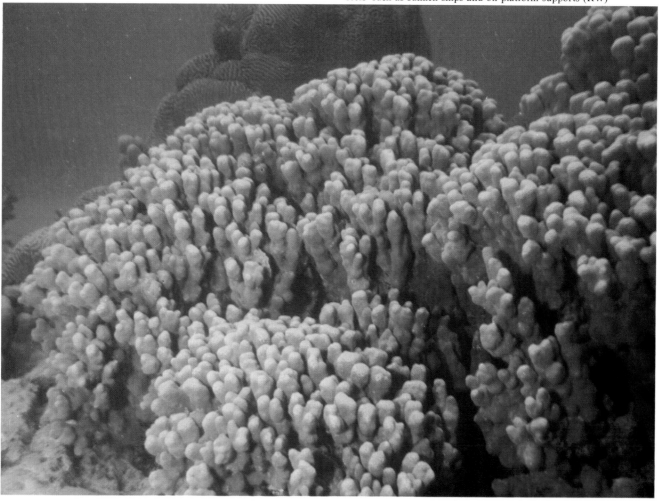

Opposite: **Coral,** a selection of different types: 1. *Porites* sp. 2. Brain coral *(Platygyra* sp.*)* 3. Honey comb coral *(Goniastrea* sp.*)* 4. Stag's horn coral *(Acropora* sp.*)* 5. *Fungia* sp. Corals 1, 2 & 4 are shown in profile with their bases to the right (ASDF)

Hermit crab *(Dardanus tinctor)*. Anenomes gain mobility and give hermit crabs extra protection in this well-known commensal relationship. Further co-operation of an astounding order is displayed when hermit crabs move to larger shells: they sometimes transfer their anenomes which release their hold on the discarded shell to facilitate the move (RW)

Coral reef fish. Several species are seen here searching for food over a *Porites* section of coral reef. Among the more visible fish are a Grey Grunt, a Jerdon's Damselfish and a Blue-striped Snapper *(Lutjanus kasmira)* (RW)

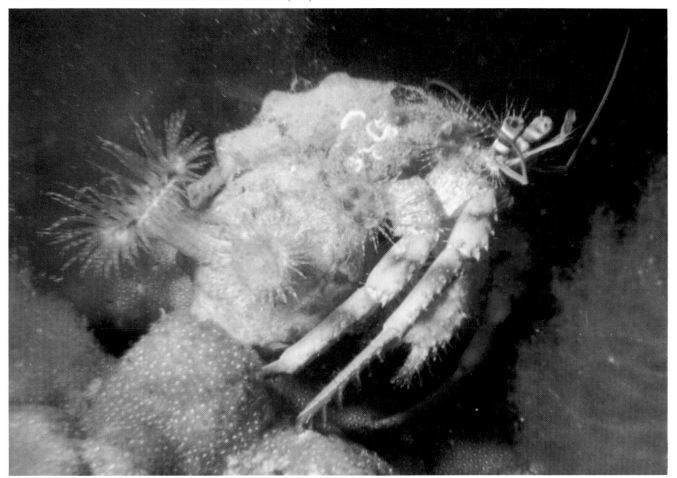

Coral reefs support an abundant and diverse fauna due largely to the productivity of the reef itself and the protection given by its crevices and crannies. Large numbers of brightly coloured fish including butterfly fish of the genus *Chaetodon* may inhabit the reef together with a wealth of invertebrates. Beautifully coloured sea slugs (Order Nudibranchia) are often to be found browsing on the surface of coral reefs together with various sea-urchins, sea-cucumbers and starfish.

Crab (Xanthidae). Many of the crabs which inhabit the coral reefs are xanthids of all shapes and sizes. This heavy-clawed specimen moving over *Porites* coral is possible prey for a dottyback (RW)

Opposite: **Sea whips** (Alcyonarian corals). Sea whips are found in deeper water generally away from the coral reefs. The skeleton is leathery and made of protein rather than calcium carbonate (ASDF)

Gulf Dottyback *(Pseudochromis persicus)*. Whilst this fish is not equipped to penetrate the defensive spines of sea urchins *(Echinometra* sp.*)* the opportunity to feed off this damaged specimen is too good to miss. The dottyback is a common fish of rock rubble and coral. Jerdon's Damselfish *(Pomacentrus sindensis)* are also seen here (RW)

Grey Grunt *(Plectorhynchus schotaf)*. Members of the Family Poma-dasyidae or grunts are common on coral reefs and rocky areas of the Gulf. The sun-dappled seabed and the fish serve to present a scene which is common to shallow water divers in Kuwait (ANHG)

Opposite: **Moray eel** *(Gymnothorax sp.)* Morays rarely emerge completely from their holes but usually lie with just the head protruding in order to snap at passing fish on which they feed (RSC)

Yellow-marked Angelfish *(Pomacanthus maculosus)*. This strikingly at-tractive species is widely distributed, being found in the Red Sea and along the east coast of Africa. Many Chaetodonts have different juvenile and adult markings. The juvenile of this species has a number of fine light bands across the body and the yellow band is not as pronounced as in this adult specimen (ANHG)

Sail-finned Surgeonfish *(Zebrasoma xanthurum)*. Despite being partially hidden, the bright yellow tail of this blue-bodied fish makes it easy to identify as a Sail-finned Surgeonfish. It is a herbivore and so is not in competition with the corallivorous butterflyfish *(Chaetodon malapterus)* close by (ANHG)

Kuwait's offshore islands are important nesting sites for a number of seabirds and have also been used by turtles in the past. Certainly several of the Saudi reef islands are still important turtle nesting sites for both the Green Turtle *(Chelonia mydas)* and the Hawksbill Turtle *(Eretmochelys imbricata)*. Both species are seen in Kuwait waters from time to time and are sometimes accidentally caught by fishermen.

Among the other marine reptiles in the Gulf are at least five species of sea-snakes (Family Hydrophiidae), a typical feature of shallow inshore waters and coral reefs. The commonest species are probably the greyish-green banded snakes *Hydrophis lapemoides* and *Hydrophis cyanocinctus*. Some give birth to live young in the water whilst others still return to land to lay their eggs on the beach. Although sea-snakes are normally very reluctant to bite, they are extremely venomous to human beings and are best left alone.

Sea slug (Opisthobranchia). Most of these shell-less molluscs are extremely beautifully marked and should be handled with care because their secretions can cause irritation (MD)

Opposite: **Sea-snake** *(Hydrophis* sp.*)* attacking a yemyam *(Helotes sexlineatus)*. Sea-snakes generally feed on young fish. The snake's tail is laterally compressed in order to provide a larger surface area for propulsion through the water (ASDF)

Loggerhead Turtle *(Caretta caretta)*. This is probably the largest species likely to be encountered in Kuwait, although the Leathery Turtle *(Dermochelys coriacea)* has occasionally been reported elsewhere in the Arabian Gulf (ANHG)

Pools & Creeks

Ephemeral pools and coastal creeks and lagoons have close affinities in terms of environment and species present in them. Rainfall in the desert, although sporadic, may on occasion be extremely heavy and result in areas of standing water, which will evaporate within days or weeks. Such ephemeral or temporary pools of water are often quite saline and, with evaporation, may eventually reach saturation point. During their short life these pools may develop dense populations of a limited variety of species that survive the drought and extremes of temperature as resistant cysts or spores in the sand. The wind also plays an important role in carrying these resting stages, and spores of halophilic or salt-tolerant bacteria and blue-green algae may be blown into these ephemeral bodies of water. Often the lowest level of the food chain is occupied by photosynthetic sulphur bacteria. These bacteria and the blue-green algae of the genera *Oscillatoria, Spirulina* and *Nitzschia* provide the food for two species of highly specialised Crustacea.

Opposite: **Pistol shrimp** (Alpheidae). Pistol shrimps are so-called because of the loud cracking noise that they make with one of their claws. One claw is normal whilst the other has a locking mechanism that prevents the claw from closing. Whilst under tension the locking mechanism is released with the result that the two halves of the claw snap quickly together (ASDF)

Ocypode crab *(Cleistostoma dotilliforme)*. This small crab (2 cm across the shell) produces extensive burrows in soft mud and muddy sand at or above high water mark. The burrow entrances usually have a lip around the edge (DAC)

Ostracod. Length 2mm. Often found in ephemeral pools in the desert, ostracods also have drought-resistant resting stages which can tolerate extremes of temperature and desication (ASDF)

Opposite: **Brine shrimp.** Length 12 mm. After heavy rain in the desert large numbers of brine shrimp may sometimes appear in pools of brackish water. The shrimps' life cycle is completed within a few weeks and the adults perish when the pools finally dry up. Drought-resistant eggs remain behind, however, lying in the sand until the next rainfall. The eggs may remain dormant for twenty years or more (ASDF)

Of these, the brine shrimp, *Artemia salina,* is commonly used by aquarists and fish farmers for feeding young fish and may reach very high densities under optimum conditions. When conditions are favourable, this species reproduces ovoviviparously: the young hatching from eggs whilst they are still in the mother. When high salinities are reached, the females produce resistant cysts which are carried by the animals until the pool dries up completely. The cysts are released from the body of the female shrimp when it disintegrates and may remain dormant in the sand for many years before favourable conditions return and stimulate the cysts to develop. Another rather spectacular crustacean, *Triops cancriformis,* may also appear in small numbers. This animal has a strong resemblance to the extinct trilobites and, like the brine shrimp, reproduces quickly only to provide resistant cysts that again may lie dormant for many years.

Ostracod. Length 1. 5mm. Relatives of the shrimps and crabs, ostracods have two shells which superficially makes them appear similar to bivalve molluscs. The empty shells can sometimes be found lying in the loose sand in dried up pools (ASDF)

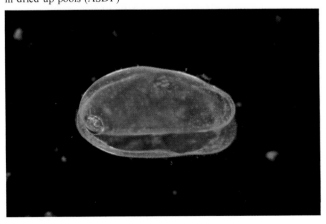

The environments of coastal creeks and lagoons are usually more harsh than that of the sea. Along the Kuwait coastline there are only two creeks, Khor Al-A'ma and Khor Al-Mufateh, near Khiran. Both of these are connected to the sea and some tidal exchange takes place. However, salinity steadily increases inland until it reaches 5 to 6 %. At the entrance to the creeks the flora and fauna are essentially the same as those on any sandy beach, but further inland fewer and fewer species are present and those that remain are an integral part of the hypersaline environment. Large areas of algal mats *(Microcoleus* sp. and *Chroococcus* sp.) are present in the area, although these are only fully submerged at spring tides. Burrowing crabs including *Cleistostoma dotilliforme* and *Eurycarcinus orientalis* abound, feeding on the relatively high productivity of the area. In this type of environment productivity is often limited because of the lack of fresh nutrients from sources such as river systems. Relatively few species of fish live in the inland parts of either of the creeks, although in the outer regions an interesting commensal association may be observed where gobies and pistol shrimps share the same burrows.

The Strandline

Virtually everyone who walks along a beach starts to collect odd bits and pieces which have been washed up and deposited along the strandline. Apart from the usual debris originating from human activities, a large proportion of the strandline material is of marine interest. Baulks of timber which have been floating in the sea for some time may have been invaded by various borers such as shipworms *(Teredo* sp.*)*. Floating objects, timber, ropes, floats and light bulbs may sometimes carry goose barnacles *(*genus *Lepas)* on their undersides which have been continuously immersed. Cuttlefish 'bones' are a common sight as indeed are the egg cases of some types of marine gastropods.

The bleached parts of various sea-urchins may be washed up, particularly the stronger and flatter parts of the burrowing sand dollar *(Clypeaster* sp.*)*. At certain times of the year, often after storms, large masses of seaweed (genus *Sargassum)* may be washed in. These species, although starting

Cuttlefish 'bone' *(Sepia officinalis)*. This is the highly modified remnant of the typical molluscan shell, totally enclosed within the body of the cuttlefish. The underside of the shell (right) is porous and contains air to provide buoyancy (ASDF)

Beachcombing. An amazing variety of objects are cast up by the sea and they usually accumulate at the high tide mark to form the strandline. Apart from the usual debris arising from human activities many of the objects are of marine origin and of interest to the naturalist (ASDF)

life attached to rock, survive equally well as attached or floating weed. Another marine alga that is very noticeable at certain times of the year is *Phaeocystis pouchii*, and occasionally, what appears to be a layer of oil on the surface of the sea is actually a dense population of this species. The large, water filled, pale yellowish-brown globules, up to 10 cm in diameter but usually 1-3 cm, may be washed up on the beach to produce an obvious scum when their numbers are very high.

Somewhat similar to these brown globules are the gelatinous bodies of ctenophores (comb jellies), which are visible only in outline since they are quite colourless and perfectly transparent. Less common are the occasional true jellyfish which may be stranded on the shore. Most species are either harmless or mildly poisonous but are best left alone unless one is familiar with them.

Last, but by no means least, are the enormous numbers of mollusc shells of all types that are washed up on the beach. There are probably about 500 different species without even including any of the small types. Most people collect shells at some time or other and the next chapter is specifically devoted to describing the commoner forms encountered in Kuwait.

Sea-urchin tests. Various types of sea urchin tests (shells) may be found washed up on the beach. 1. *Prionocidaris baculosa* with long robust spines (note the ball and socket attachment) 2. *Echinometra mathaei*. 3. Sand dollar *(E. auritus)* with spines 4. Sand dollar *(Clypeaster reticulatus)* without spines 5. Sand dollar *(Echinodiscus auritus)* without spines (ASDF)

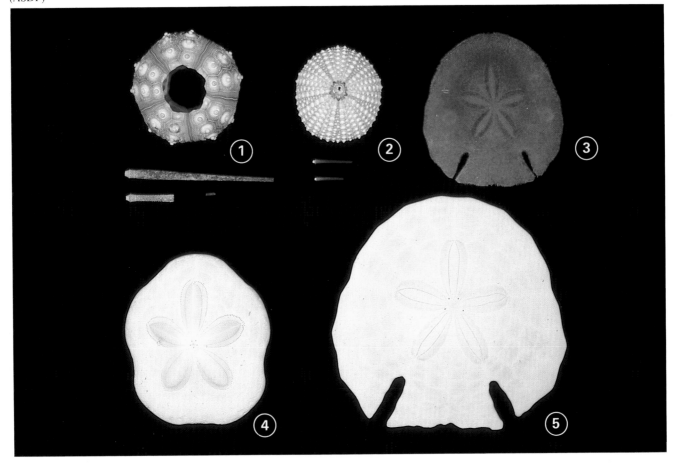

Seashells

By
Michael Deeks and Charles Johnson
Charles Johnson was responsible for the selection and preparation of the shells in the composite plates.

Title page: **Fishbone Murex,** *Murex scolopax* (ASDF)

S eashells are the homes of softbodied marine animals called molluscs. The limy shell is secreted by the animal usually to protect it and to give it support, but it plays no part in the metabolism of the animal. Consequently many successful molluscs have no shell whatsoever. The majority of creatures in this large group or phylum, the second largest in the animal kingdom, live in the sea or fresh water, but there are numerous terrestrial forms such as the garden snail or slug. Many of the animals are very beautiful, but it is usually by the great diversity of their shells that we know them. Indeed the shells still play an important part in the identification of molluscs, despite great advances in our knowledge of their anatomy.

Spindle shell *(Fusinus townsendi)*. Living in the zone of shifting tides, many inshore molluscs are rolled and washed about by the moving waters. Here a spindle shell is trying to right itself after having been upturned. The operculum can clearly be seen at the end of the extended foot and the fleshy flap encircling the body inside the shell is the mantle, the part of the animal which secretes the shell (DAC & CTJ)

The Mollusca includes the Scaphopoda (tooth or tusk shells) and the Cephalopoda (squids, cuttlefish, octopus), but nearly all the shells found on the beach belong to the two largest classes: the Gastropoda and the Bivalvia. The gastropods, or univalves, have a single shell, usually like that of a snail, which can take on a bewildering variety of forms. The bivalves (clams, scallops, oysters) secrete a shell in two parts, or valves, joined together by a ligament which acts as a hinge.

The typical gastropod or snail form is an animal with a large, muscular foot on which it crawls and a well developed head with a snout or proboscis, tentacles and eyes. Gastropods may be vegetarian or carnivorous. In the bivalves or clam-like types, the animal has a large elongate or hatchet-shaped foot, but no head parts as such. This is because these creatures do not actively search for food but feed by filtering out micro-organisms from the water or from the mud and sand of the sea floor. All marine molluscs breathe with the aid of gills which are usually supplied with water by some sort of siphon - a fleshy respiratory tube.

Although some marine shells float on the surface and others live in the abyssal (deep sea) world, the vast majority inhabit the littoral and sub-littoral zones, that is along the intertidal shore line and in waters down to a depth of approximately 100 m. Within this vertical distribution molluscs are to be found in virtually every marine habitat. Many species, particularly among the bivalves, are adapted for burrowing and will thus be found on sandy or muddy shores. Other forms are well adapted to rocky shores or coral reefs; some affix themselves to rocks or coral, others take refuge under them, and yet others bore into rock, sponge or coral and live inside.

There are probably about 500 different species of marine molluscs in Kuwait, approximately half of which are under 1 cm in length. A keen collector can therefore build up a collection of a hundred or more species without even including any of the small types. Most people collect shells at some time or another, but not many think about the creatures which live inside. Molluscs lead diverse and interesting lives and some knowledge of their activities and means of survival enhances a visit to the beach.

In this perspective, then, let us now take a look at a few of Kuwait's more typical shells in the general

Cuttlefish *(Sepia* sp.*)*. Cuttlefish are very common cephlopods in the Arabian Gulf, being found on coral reefs, in rocky areas and over grassbeds (RW)

Persian Conch *(Strombus decorus persicus)*. Endemic to the Gulf, this conch is sometimes mistaken for a cone shell. Here the animal is reaching out with its foot to dig its operculum into the sand and right itself. Spectacular and prominent eyes at the ends of long peduncles vary in colour from one species to another. The stromboid notch in the lip of the shell allows the right eye stalk to protrude when the animal is withdrawn. The balloon-like green alga *(Colpomenia sinuosa)* on the right is attached to the shell, but does not hinder this active herbivore's mobility (DAC & CTJ)

context of their habitat. It should be remembered, however, that some of the more active, mobile snail forms may be found living in more than one kind of habitat or seabed condition.

The accompanying colour plates show examples of all the shell types discussed in the text and include some other species as well.

Scaphopods

Scaphopods or tusk shells are so-called because of their resemblance to elephants' tusks. These creatures are quite primitive, having no head or eyes; they live with the wider end of the shell anchored by the foot in the sand and the narrower end, containing the exhalant siphon, protruding from the surface.

Sand-dwelling Gastropods

Most topshells are conical and, as their name suggests, resemble a child's spinning top. Button topshells *(Umbonium vestiarium)* are members of the same family, but are unusually flattened. They are very pretty and quite common, although they often pass unnoticed because of their small size. At low water there may be numerous squiggles or doodles in the sand left by button topshells in their search for the microscopic food between sand grains.

The dogwhelk *(Nassarius arcularius plicatus)* and the dove shell *(Mitrella blanda)* are both very common and are frequently found in colonies on the same beach. They leave tracks similar to those of the button topshells, but are carnivores and can be watched busily searching for food, usually carrion, with their long probosces. The spindle

Tusk shells and sand-dwelling gastropods.: 1. Tusk shells *(Dentalium* sp., *Dentalium octangulatum)* 2. Button topshell *(Umbonium vestiarium)* 3. Dogwhelk *(Nassarius arcularius plicatus)* 4. Speckled Moonshell *(Natica pulicaris)* 5. Carrier shell *(Xenophora corrugata)* 6. Banded mitre shell *(Vexillum osiridis)* (syn. *Pusia osiridis*) 7. Spindle shell *(Fusinus townsendi)* 8. Dove shell *(Mitrella blanda)* 9. Auger shell *(Terebra* sp.*)* (ASDF)

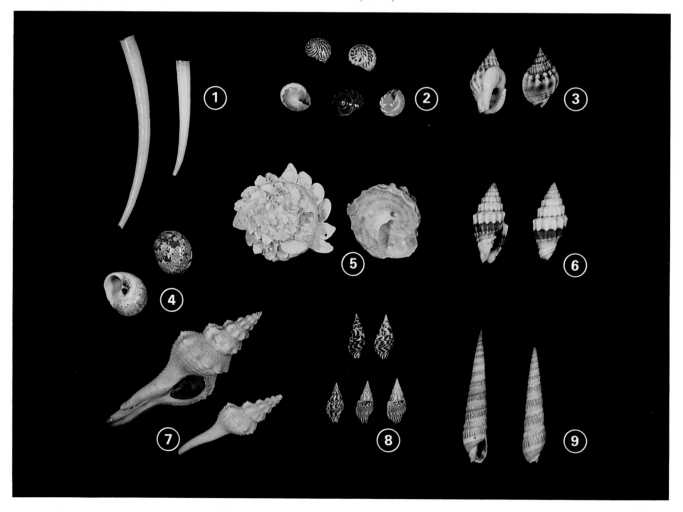

shell *(Fusinus townsendi)* lives in smaller groups and prefers live prey. The animal is a brilliant orange in colour.

Members of the Family Naticidae are commonly known as moonshells or necklace shells. The second name is given to them because of the unusual way in which they deposit their eggs: sand grains are incorporated into a necklace or ribbon-like band of eggs, which is firm but pliable. These curved egg ribbons can sometimes be seen washed up on sandy beaches. The moonshell is a carnivore and burrows in the sand hunting for small bivalves and gastropods. It holds the prey with its large foot, drills a neat hole through the shell and then rasps out the meat with its radula or 'tongue'. The shell of the live mollusc is glossy due to the fact that for much of the time it is enveloped by the mantle, a wide flap around the body of the mollusc. All shelled molluscs have a mantle although in some species it can be rather small. This organ secretes the shell and, as in the case of the moonshell and others, sometimes covers it, thereby protecting it from abrasion.

Moonshells and other gastropods. 1. Tinted moonshell *(Polinices powisiana)*, 2. Paper moonshell *(Eunaticina papilla)*, 3. Lined moonshell *(Natica lineata)*, 4. False moonshell *(Vanikoro sulcata)*, 5. Wormshell *(Serpulorbis sulcatus)*. The wormshell and false moonshell live on rocks, whereas the true moonshells are all sand-dwellers (ASDF)

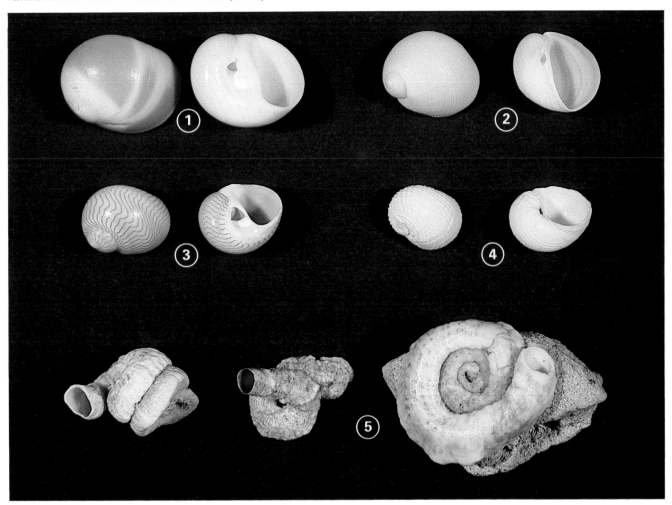

The carrier shell *(Xenophora corrugata)* attaches the shells of other molluscs and small stones to its own shell. The fragments are picked up with a part of the foot and attached to the shell by a secretion from a gland in the foot. It is not known why this is done, but it is thought unlikely to be for camouflage since some species live in deep water where there is little light. It has been suggested that the attached fragments are to reinforce the shell or that they serve to enlarge the shell base and thus prevent it sinking into a soft seabed. The carrier shell does not crawl over the seabed but moves in a series of leaps. Many gastropods have a horny operculum or trapdoor to plug their shell and the carrier shell also uses this to aid movement. To move, it thrusts out its foot, jabs the operculum into the sand for anchorage and then jerks itself forward. Carrier shells are unusual in that they can be caught live with a rod and line.

The mitre shell takes its name from the resemblance of some species to a bishop's headdress. It burrows in the sand with the siphon extended, but can also be found under rocks. The snout is long and retractable and used for feeding on worms, bivalves and carrion.

Auger shells (Terebridae) live mostly in sandy habitats and burrow just below the surface, leaving a characteristic ridged track. Some possess a poison apparatus similar to that of the cone shells, a large, related group very seldom found on Kuwait's beaches, but living offshore.

Well known on sandy beaches throughout the Gulf is the pretty *Ancilla castenea,* one of the two olive

Chestnut olive shell *(Ancilla castenea).* A striking example of colour variation in a single species is shown here and on the opposite page (ASDF)

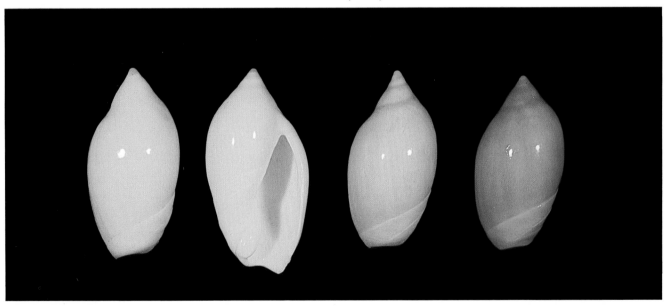

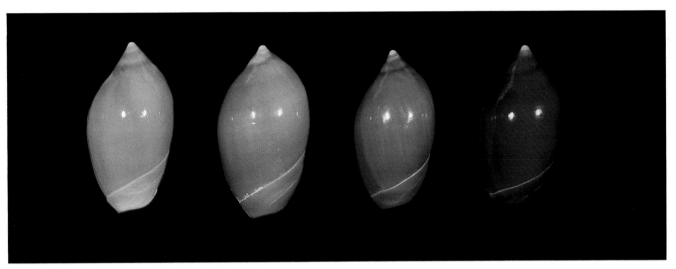

Chestnut olive shell *(Ancilla castenea).* A striking example of colour variation in a single species is shown here and on the opposite page (ASDF)

Chestnut olive shell *(A. castenea).* In certain species the animal is more beautiful than its shell. Here the snail's mantle is only somewhat extended, but the animal's typical colouring, which varies less than the colour of the shell, is well in view. Active at night, this olive shell is almost never seen crawling about since during the day it burrows down as much as three inches under the sand (GR)

shells commonly found in Kuwait. Although the shell can vary from pure white to dark brown, most of the individuals living in a given area will have the same general colour.

Conches (Strombidae) also use the operculum as an aid to locomotion, but their operculum is long, pointed, sickle-shaped and has a serrated edge on one side. It is too narrow to act as a trapdoor to the shell, but is perfectly adapted as a lever and is also used as a defensive weapon against predators. The Persian Conch *(Strombus decorus persicus)* is very common on Kuwait's beaches and snorkelers may see large numbers of them. They leave characteristic tracks in the sand, rather larger than those of the button topshells. Conches are noted for a notch on the lower outer lip of the shell through which the animal can protrude its colourful stalked right eye in order to keep a lookout whilst feeding. They are all herbivores, feeding on algae and plant detritus.

Terebellum terebellum is a conch that appears to have none of the features generally associated with the family. The shell is fairly small and thin and without either a stromboid notch or a broad lip. The animal, however, is anatomically similar to the other members of the group. *T. terebellum* is a burrower, its torpedo-shaped shell being admirably suited to this purpose and whilst it is burrowing a watch is kept with one or other of its stalked eyes protruding from the sand. It can also shoot rapidly through the water by expelling water under pressure from its siphon.

The long and slender Arabian Tibia *(Tibia insulaechorab curta),* with its finger-like projections, can be seen on Failaka but is usually found living

Opposite. **Sand-dwelling gastropods.** 1. Persian conch *(Strombus decorus persicus)* 2. Torpedo conch *(Terebellum terebellum)* 3. Arabian Tibia *(Tibia insulaechorab curta)* 4. Fishbone murex *(Murex scolopax)* 5. Bonnet shell *(Phalium faurotis)* 6. Bubble shell *(Bulla ampulla)* (ASDF)

Fishbone murex *(Murex scolopax)*. A vivid illustration of differences in mature size in a given species. The smaller specimen is an average-sized adult. whereas the exceptionally large one measures 144 mm (ASDF) offshore. It is also a member of the Family Strombidae, and although it lacks the typical stromboid notch, it does have a broad, thick and winglike lip at the entrance to the shell, which is another general feature of conch shells. The thin needle-like extension from the base of the shell is recessed and carries the animal's inhalant siphon.

The Fishbone murex *(Murex scolopax)* is relatively common in Kuwait and fragments of its shell can be found on most sandy beaches. It is a member of the large and attractive Family Muricidae, which is characterised by shells often having long spines and/or extensive frills. This species lives in shallow water on sandy bottoms. It can burrow, but can be spotted because the tip of the siphonal canal often protrudes from the sand. This murex preys on bivalves and forces the valves apart, using its foot as a suction pad and the teeth on the lip of its shell as a lever. Mollusc shells do not grow continuously but in stages and the murex

Frog shells. Although seldom seen washed up on the beach, these gastropods are occasionally taken offshore in Kuwait by shrimp trawlers. The large specimen is *Bursa spinosa;* the smaller one is probably a different species (ASDF)

is a good example of this. Each spiny ridge represents the end of a growth period. The spines are formed by the secretion of projections in the mantle.

Bonnet shells *(Phalium faurotis)* are members of the helmet shell family (Cassidae). Rather surprisingly, their favourite food is sea-urchins or other echinoderms and they are able to secrete an acid solution through their long snout or proboscis, which both softens the shell and paralyses the animal, enabling them to bore into it. The bonnet shell can then cut out and eat large pieces of its immobilised prey.

The bubble shell *(Bulla ampulla)* is a carnivore that swallows its prey whole, shell included. Strong calcareous plates in its stomach grind and crush the shell of the prey so that it can be digested. The large mantle almost completely covers the shell, keeping it glossy.

Rock-dwelling gastropods. 1. Murex *(Hexaplex kuesterianus)* 2. Variable Thais *(Thais mutabilis)* 3. *Rapana bulbosa* (ASDF)

Rock-dwelling gastropods. 1. Graceful Cowry *(Cypraea gracilis)* 2. Freckled Cowry *(Cypraea lentiginosa)* 3. Onyx Cowry *(Cypraea onyx succincta)* 4. Thrush Cowry *(Cypraea turdus)*(ASDF)

Rock-dwelling Gastropods

Cowries (Family Cypraeidae) have a large mantle that extends over the shell from both sides to secrete the beautiful glossy patterns for which the family is known. Three of these exotic shells can be found live on the shores of Kuwait: *Cypraea turdus, Cypraea lentiginosa* and *Cypraea gracilis*. The otherwise common *Cypraea onyx succincta* is rarely seen alive here, although its dead shell, like those of yet three other cowry species, is occasionally washed up on the beach. Cowries are nocturnal and depending on the species, feed on coral polyps, algae, hydroids or animal detritus. The females incubate their eggs, which is not common amongst molluscs. The juvenile shell is not always recognized as a cowry, for its aperture may have teeth on only one side or none at all. It is also much lighter than the adult, but becomes progressively heavier as more and more layers of shell are deposited on the outer surface by the

Opposite: **Thrush Cowry** *(Cypraea turdus)*. This animal is almost fully extended, showing the finely branching papillae on the mantle, a distinctive feature common to the entire cowry family (ASDF)

Freckled Cowries *(Cypraea lentiginosa)*. Seen here in their natural habitat the cowry on the left has its mantle fully extended with the whitish papillae in view. The tentacles of this species are orangish in colour. Like many other molluscs, these shy creatures are nocturnal feeders and are rarely seen during the day (DAC & CTJ)

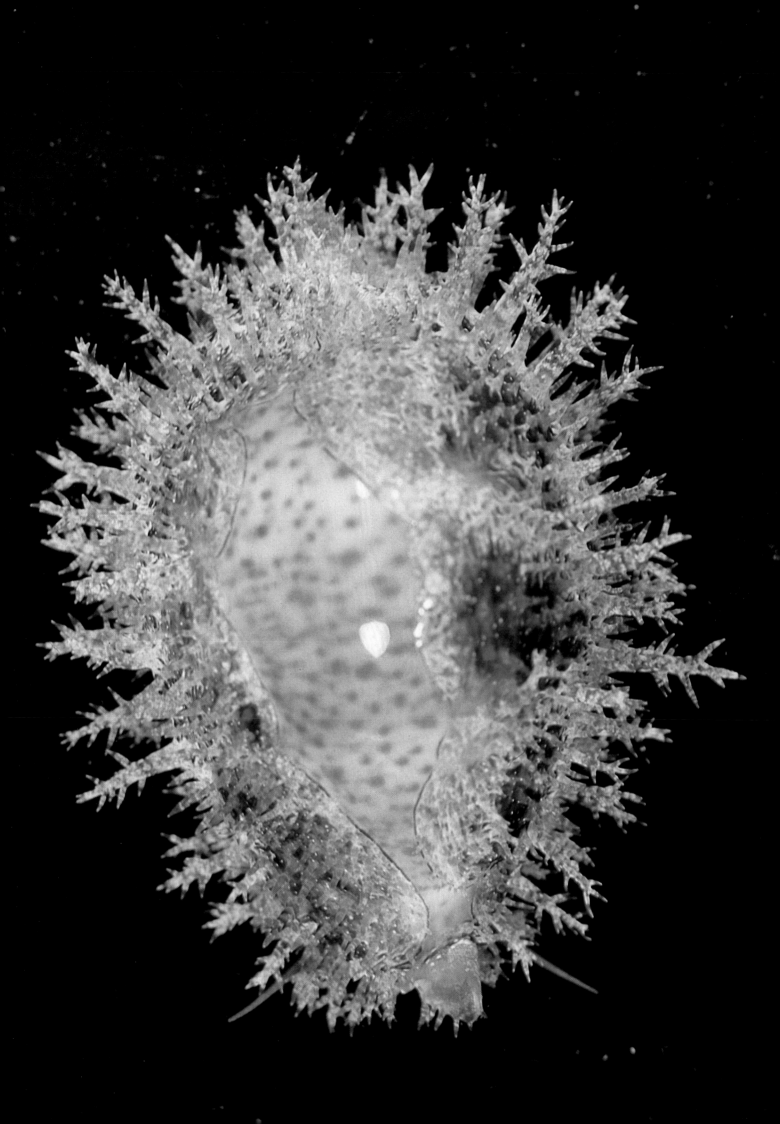

mantle. Frequently different layers have differently coloured patterns and this can be seen in the worn shells cast up on Kuwait's beaches.

Many species of the murex superfamily (Muricacea) are found in rocky habitats. *Hexaplex kuesterianus,* with its heavy spines, is a typical representative. The closely related Thaididae, often referred to as rock shells, have strong knobbly shells with crenulate apertures. *Thais mutabilis* lives in the intertidal zone and is a carnivore as are all the muricids. Thais shells of the genus *Rapana* are particularly voracious, as the name suggests, and prey on barnacles, bivalves, and even conches.

Banded nutmeg *(Cancellaria* sp.*).* This shell was collected after having been washed up on the beach at Failaka. It is one of two specimens known to have been found in Kuwait (ASDF)

Slipper limpet *(Crepidula walshi)* and two **Pheasant shells** *(Phasianella solida).* The slipper limpet lives attached to other shells. The pheasant shell likes a fine sand bottom, often about midway between the high and low tide lines (ASDF)

Opposite: **Limpets, topshells and others.** 1. Keyhole limpet *(Diodora funiculata)* 2. Banded Horn Shell *(Cerithidea cingulata)* 3. Streaked topshell *(Trochus erythraeus).* 4. False limpet *(Siphonaria rosea)* 5. Turban shell *(Turbo coronatus)* 6. Strawberry topshell *(Clanculus pharaonius).* The Banded Horn Shell lives in sand or mud, the others are all rock dwellers (ASDF)

Clusterwink *(Planaxis sulcatus).* Living on rocks near the high tide line, this gastropod can withstand long periods of time out of the water (ASDF)

Staircase nutmeg *(Trigonostoma scalariformis = ? Cancellaria costifera).* An uncommon gastropod, this species is sometimes found hidden in sand pockets on rock beds (ASDF)

No true limpets are commonly found on Kuwait's shores, although false limpets (Siphonariidae) and keyhole limpets (Fissurellidae) may be seen. Keyhole limpets remain firmly attached to the rocks in the daytime and by night move away to browse on algae, whereas false limpets move about and feed only when they are exposed by the falling tide. The hole or slit in the keyhole limpet is an outlet for waste.

Turban shells (Turbinidae) such as *Turbo coronatus* are related to the topshells but the operculum is thick, heavy and calcareous instead of horny. *T.*

Rock cerith *(Cerithium caeruleum)*. This rock dweller can be found in population densities in excess of 100 per square metre (ASDF)

Three-ribbed Capshell *(Amathina tricostata)*. This curious gastropod usually lives subtidally attached to rock or coral-dwelling bivalves such as the Thorny oyster, the Rock scallop or the Pearl oyster. It attaches itself directly to the bivalve shell or rock instead of secreting a calcareous plate underneath itself as do certain other forms (ASDF)

Variegated thais *(Thais savignyi)*. A common intertidal carnivore, this Thais lives on rocks in exposed areas (ASDF)

Pearly Baby's ear *(Stomatella sulcifera)*. The most common of the three or so species of Stomatella found in Kuwait, this shy gastropod lives attached to the undersides of rocks in the intertidal zone (ASDF)

coronatus can be seen living in thousands on Kuwait's rocky beaches and is the only turban shell commonly found on the shore. Like the topshells, the turbans are vegetarians.

Ceriths and horn shells (Cerithidae) can be found in most habitats, among rocks and debris, in weed or on sandy shores. They are mostly scavengers, with small, strong, elongated shells. A common sand- or mud-dweller in Kuwait is the pretty little Banded Horn Shell *(Cerithidea cingulata)*.

Trochus erythraeus is the largest of the several species of topshell (Trochidae) living on Kuwait's rocky shores. The strawberry topshell *(Clanculus pharaonius)* is also found here, although it is more common in the Indian Ocean.

Rock & Coral-dwelling Bivalves

Like most bivalves, the scallops (Pectinidae) feed by catching small particles of food in their gills when they inhale. Some scallops can swim by snapping their valves together whilst others, such as *Chlamys ruschenbergerii,* are fixed to rocks or coral by a byssus. This is a tuft of silky threads secreted by the foot of the bivalve and attached by the tip of the foot to the substrate. Scallops are best observed under water, for the fringe of the mantle is studded with brightly coloured 'eyes'.

Screw shell *(Turritella ?auricincta)* and on the right **Turrid shell** *(Inquisitor griffithi)*. These gastropods live in sandy or somewhat silty seabeds. This species of turrid is the largest found in the Gulf but is rarely seen live intertidally (ASDF)

False Ormer *(Stomatia phymotis)*. The animal of this curious snail looks like light-purple velvet and blends in with the rock surfaces to which it clings - the shell being covered with marine growths. When fully extended, the foot is enormously larger than the shell (ASDF)

Speckled mitre *(Mitra bovei)*. An elusive species, this animal is pure white and can conceal itself completely in a very small quantity of sand. The specimen on the right shows the colouration of a beach-worn shell (ASDF)

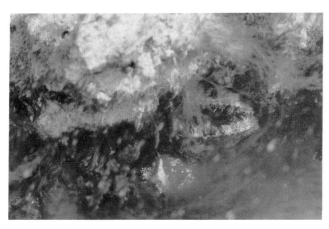

Scallop *(Chlamys rushenbergerii)*. Shown here in a typical habitat, the scallop has its valves agape taking in the oxygenated water brought in by the incoming tide. The fleshy mantle filaments near the edge of each valve are well in view. A fixed species, this scallop attaches itself to the hard substrate of both rock and coral reef crevices (DAC & CTJ)

Opposite: **Rock and coral-dwelling bivalves.** 1. Scallop *(Chlamys ruschenbergerii)* 2. Pearl oyster *(Pinctada margaritifera)* 3. Wing oyster *(Pteria marmorata)* 4. Thorny oyster *(Spondylus gaederopus)* 5. Jewel-box shell *(Chama pacifica)* 6. Arc shell *(Anadara ehrenbergi)* (ASDF)

Pen shells *(Pinna muricata)* in their natural environment. Normally only the edges of the valves protrude from the sand. The plants are *Halophila uninervis* (ASDF)

Pearl oysters (Pteriidae) sometimes occur in extensive beds. They have been fished in the Gulf for their pearls for centuries, but the trade has diminished since the introduction of Japanese cultured pearls and the decline in the numbers of pearl divers. The related wing oyster *(Pteria marmorata.)* has a more fragile shell with long winglike projections at the hinge.

Thorny oysters (Spondylidae) live in habitats similar to those of attached scallops. The name is misleading since this mollusc is not an oyster at all, but is closely related to the scallop. *Spondylus gaederopus* attaches one of its valves permanently to rock or coral by a calcareous secretion. Many spines and 'ears', usually of bright colours, grow from the top valve, which is the flatter of the two.

Chama pacifica is a member of the Chamidae or jewel-box family. It attaches itself to rocks by a limey secretion and on first inspection may appear to be a thorny oyster.

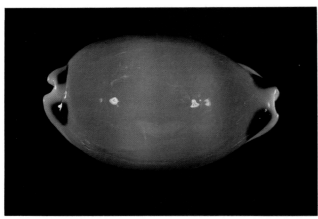

Brown-eyed Cowry *(Cypraea pulchra)*. Length 70 mm. Found at a depth of 12 m., this beautiful cowry is one of Kuwait's larger coral reef gastropods. The animal has a nearly black foot and mantle with no visible papillae (ASDF & CTJ)

Arc shells (Arcidae) such as *Anadara ehrenbergi* are unusual because of the large area of shell around the hinge line and the straight line of numerous interlocking hinge teeth. Many species have a byssus and attach themselves to rocks.

Sand & Mud-dwelling Bivalves

Pen shells *(Pinna muricata)* are large, thin and fragile and frequently encrusted with marine growth. They anchor themselves vertically in the sand by a byssus. In Kuwait the shells can grow to approximately 30 cm in length.

At home in Kuwait's more sheltered muddy bottoms is the Window-pane Oyster, *Placuna placenta,* a member of the saddle oyster family and usually found in very large colonies. It is thin, flat, almost circular, translucent and nearly colourless. The shell is anchored by a byssus plug when young, but as an adult it is free to move. Its name is derived from its use in south-east Asia for glazing windows.

The razor shell or jack-knife clam (Solenidae) lives in soft mud and sand. It is a filter feeder and is normally hidden from sight with both its inhalant and exhalant siphon just level with the surface of the mud. The smooth, light and narrow shell is perfectly adapted for burrowing and if the slightest pressure is applied to the mud nearby the mollusc will bury itself with exceptional speed. It does this by extending the foot from the lower part of the shell into the sand and pumping blood into it so that it swells and acts as an anchor. At the same instant, muscular contractions of the foot pull the shell valves downwards. The blood in the foot is then withdrawn, forcing the shell valves outwards and thus holding the mollusc secure against the sides of the burrow whilst the foot again extends downwards. Some razor shells are able to burrow faster than a collector can dig.

The little heart shells (Carditidae) are tough, ridged shells that favour shallow water. The ridges are sometimes ornamented as in *Cardita ffinchi*

Opposite: **Sand and mud-dwelling bivalves.** 1. Pen shell *(Pinna muricata)* 2. Window-pane oyster *(Placuna placenta)* 3. Razor shell *(Solen* sp.*)* 4. Fluted little heart shell *(Cardita ffinchi)* 5. Sunset shell *(Gari occidens)* (ASDF)

Carnelian Cowry *(Cypraea carneola)*. Length 70mm. Also found at a depth of 12m, this cowry is another of Kuwait's larger coral reef gastropods. The foot and mantle of this animal are variegated with lavender, the papillae being well developed and white (ASDF & CTJ)

and the edges of the shell are wavy or crenulate. A few attach themselves to the undersides of rocks but most species live buried in the sand, some serving as anchors for certain kinds of seaweed.

Sunset shells (Psammobiidae) are related to the Tellinidae. *Gari occidens* is a smooth shell slightly gaping at the ends and tinted a delicate pink with radial rays extending from the umbone, the small hump on each valve usually close to the hinge ligament. In this species the animal is very large and cannot completely withdraw into its shell so it lives well buried in the sand to escape predators.

As we have seen, marine molluscs are interesting not only because of their shells, but as living organisms playing an important role in virtually every habitat of the intertidal ecosystem. Indeed, although we have discussed only a few species here, the marine gastropods have some of the most diversified feeding habits of any group in the animal kingdom. Since there is still much we do not understand about these creatures, however, even the amateur naturalist can make significant contributions to our knowledge of the group, both through field study and aquarium observation.

Opposite: **Arabian Venus Clam** *(Circenita callipyga, f. arabica)*. This species, which has an enormous range of colour patterns, is one of Kuwait's most typical intertidal sand-dwelling bivalves (ASDF)

Sand-dwelling bivalves. 1. Ridged sunset shell *(Asaphis violescens)* *(A. ? deflorata)* 2. Painted little heart shell *(Cardita bicolor)* 3. Lilac trough shell *(Mactra lilacea)* 4. Rough cockle *(Trachycardium lacunosum)* 5. Brown dog cockle *(Glycymeris lividus)* 6. Ribbed dog cockle *(Glycymeris maskatensis)* (ASDF)

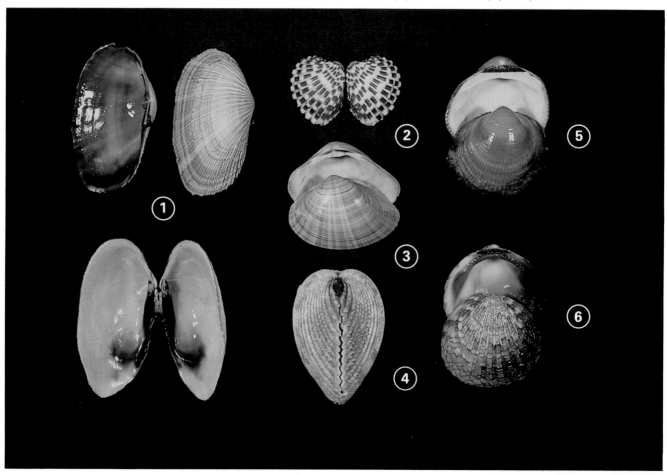

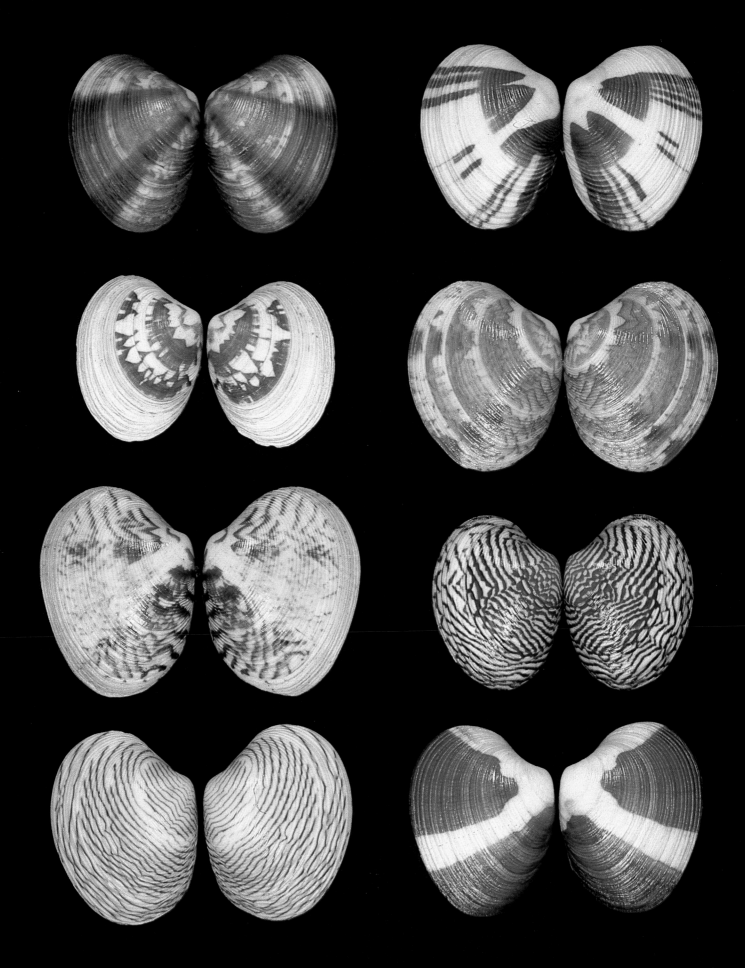

Traditional Fishing

By

Tony Farmer and

Abdul-Rahman Abdul-Ghaffar

Title page: **Goufa or scoop net** (NPvZ)

A brief introduction to the marine natural history of Kuwait would not be complete without at least some reference to fishing activities. Fishing has a long tradition in Kuwait and even today some very old, but efficient methods are still in use.

Perhaps the most obvious of the various fishing methods, at least to anyone visiting the shores of Kuwait, are the 'hadra' or stake traps. These were formerly common along the Kuwait City water-front, but have largely disappeared because of coastal development although a few remain in use between the Kuwait Towers and Shuwaikh Port.

Hadra. The end of the day at low tide, this hadra is explored by children. At high water the netting can just be seen above the surface (DPP)

In 1966 there were 225 hadra in Kuwait as a whole, but by 1974 only 99 remained. Numbers are increasing again and it is estimated that there are now about 130. These traps generally rely on tidal movements to retain the fish behind netting barriers as the tide recedes. The trapped fish are guided into the 'housh' or outer parlour and finally into the 'serr' or inner parlour from which they cannot escape. The catch is generally removed from the hadra daily at low tide using a 'misleh', a net stretched between two sticks one held in each hand. At one time the hadra were constructed of date palm mid-ribs woven to form a lattice which was set vertically in the seabed to act as a fence.

The vertical members of the lattice were usually whole mid-ribs, whilst the interwoven horizontal members were simple ropes made from date palm fibres. Sadly perhaps, the hadra are now made from galvanised wire mesh (19-22mm) and synthetic fibre ropes. The hadra are protected from the effect of tides and waves by guy rope supports attached to stakes or iron pegs driven into the seabed. These are placed at intervals along both

Opposite: **Fish market.** Prospective purchasers examining freshly caught fish displayed on the quai near the Seif Palace (CWTP)

Hadra. Stake traps are generally constructed totally within the intertidal zone. Fish are initially trapped in the outer parlour and then, as the tide recedes, in the smaller inner parlour from which the fisherman removes his catch (DAC)

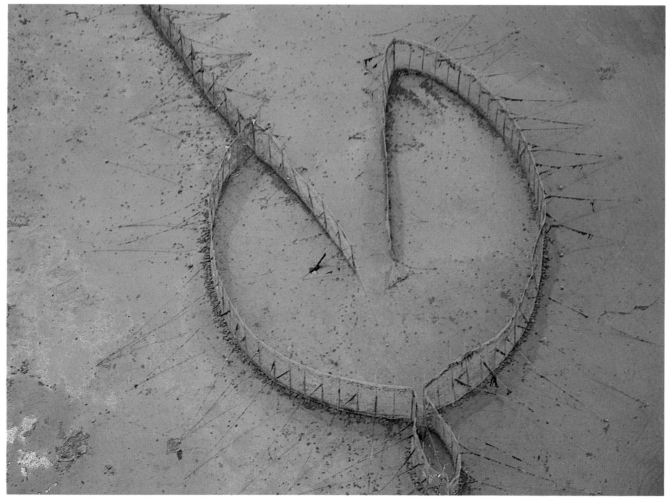

sides of the barrier or 'thraa' and the outer parlour, and only on the outside of the inner parlour.

Fishermen operating the hadra need to have an
excellent knowledge of the local tides and current
patterns in order to obtain the best results from
the traps. Local variations in the number of
parlours and the orientation of the barriers are
intended to take advantage of the local current
patterns, and hence increase the efficiency of the
traps. Hadra tend to be built in the same positions
and in the same configuration over long periods,
even by different fishermen, indicating that the
specific design of each trap is closely related to the
local conditions. Seabirds, such as cormorants
during winter, tend to perch on the hadra and take
their toll of the catch. Some fishermen erect scare-
crows over the inner parlour in order to deter such
predations. The efficiency of these traps can be
judged by the wide selection of inshore fish species
and crabs that are sold in the market place. Whilst
not all are edible, over fifty species of fish can be
taken during the course of a year, the seasons
dictating which species are the commonest in any
one catch.

Opposite: **Hadra** are a beautiful sight from the air. Only then can their
shape and orientation be fully appreciated. No two hadra are constructed
alike, each being erected to take advantage of the local terrain and the
prevailing currents and tides (ASDF)

Hadra. Beginning as a roll of netting with stakes attached, the hadra will
be erected in the sea on a specially selected site favoured by the fishermen.
In exposed areas hadra are removed from the sea and stored during the
winter to protect them from damage by heavy seas (ASDF)

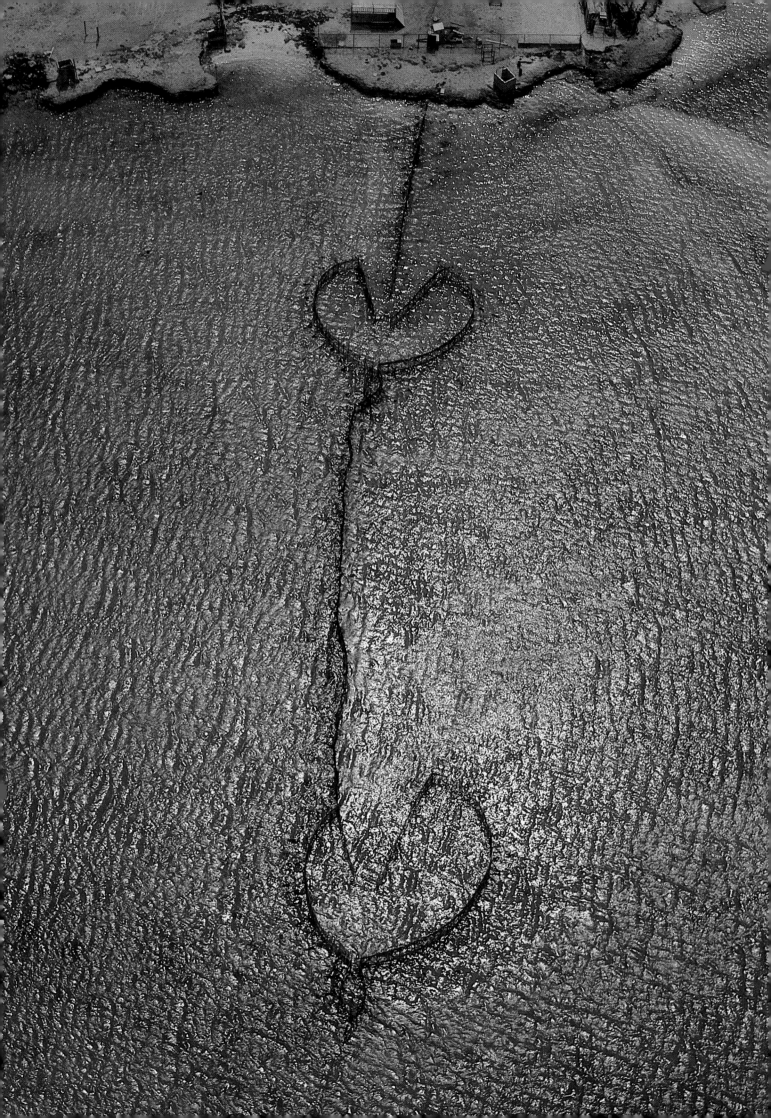

Wire fish traps similar to lobster traps are also
used in Kuwait. These are generally known as
'gargour', although they come in three sizes. The
largest of these, the 'douwaabi', has a diameter of
2.6 m across the base and a mesh size of approximately 50 mm. The two smaller types have base
diameters of 1.8 m and 1.0 m and mesh sizes of 42

Gargour. A dhow being loaded with wire traps. These are used for
catching large bottom and reef-dwelling fish such as hamoor *(Epinephelus
tauvina)*. The traps are often not marked by floats or buoys, but somehow
the fishermen manage to find them again (KJM)

mm and 35 mm respectively, and are known collectively as gargour. The fish enter the gargour through a single conical entrance let into the side of the trap which tapers in such a way that escape by the same means is extremely difficult, if not impossible, for the larger fish. Gargour were originally made from the split mid-ribs of date palm leaves, but these too have been replaced by galvanised wire. The traps are used particularly in

A medium size fish trap *(gargour)*. Note the singular circular opening leading into the woven wire mesh funnel through which the fish will enter the trap. They are unable to escape once inside (ASDF)

The circular bases of the traps douwaabi' are strengthend by using a lattice of bamboo poles (ASDF)

Completed douwaabi lying near the harbour and ready to load onto the fishing boat (ASDF)

Fishermen attaching the bamboo reinforced base to a large fish trap 'douwaabi' (ASDF)

areas of rocky bottoms or adjacent to reefs where other types of fishing gear normally cannot be used. As a result gargour usually catch reef fish such as hamour *(Epinephalus tauvina)*, hamrah *(Lutjanus coccineus)*, sobaity *(Acanthopagrus cuvieri)*, and firsh *(Plectorhynchus cinctus)*. Hamour and hamrah orientated gargour fisheries operate from Fahaheel and Nigaat Shamlaan which is adjacent to the Seif Palace. Since the base of the trap can be removed, a small speed boat can carry a surprising number of gargour by the simple expedient of stacking them one inside another.

Some of the dhows using gargour may provide a curious sight when loaded with forty or more traps piled above the deck awnings. A single boat may operate with as many as four hundred traps.

A fishing boat laden with traps *(gargour)* ready to sail for the fishing grounds (ASDF)

Weights are tied to the base of the gargour in the final preparatory stages (ASDF)

Taroof. Fishermen are seen here preparing a gill net. Floats and weights have to be attached to the top and bottom edges of the net to make it hang correctly in the water. Very fine green twine is generally used for the meshes, as it is unlikely to be seen by the fish before they become entangled in the net (ASDF)

Set nets are a common sight in Kuwait waters and are chiefly used for fishing the highly prized zobaidy *(Pampus argenteus)*. These nets are now generally operated from small speed boats. The two basic types of set nets used in Kuwait are the 'taroof' which is used primarily in shallow waters, and the 'leekh' or 'iddah' which is used in much deeper areas.

The taroof is usually about 50 m in length, 2.8 m deep and has a mesh size of about 40-90 mm. The leekh can vary from 48 m to 58 m in length and is 2.4 - 3.2 m deep with a mesh size of 40-70 mm. To maintain the nets' vertical position in the water they are provided with floats along one edge and lead weights along the other. Formerly the floats were the flat bases of date palm leaves and the weights were stones. The set nets work on the gill net principle: fish swim into the vertically suspended net and become caught by the gill covers or opercula. Each taroof fisherman may operate as many as 10-12 separate nets per boat. The leekh is

Speed boat harbour. There are several small harbours in Kuwait, this one is adjacent to the National Assembly Building. These boats are generally used by the tarouf or leekh gill netters or the gargour fishermen (ASDF)

Gill nets *(leekh)* stored ready for the next fishing trip. The floats and weights of a 'leekh' are generally larger than those of a 'taroof' (ASDF)

Old floats made from the leaf bases of date palms. These were formerly used for gill nets. *(leekh and taroof)* (ASDF)

usually more heavily weighted than the taroof and fished in strings of up to 70 nets which may extend as far as 4 km. Apart from zobaidy, both types of net are used for catching khubbat *(Scomberomorus guttatus)*, suboor *(Hilsa ilisha)*, maid *(Liza macrolepis)* and beyah *(Valamugil seheli)*.

Cast nets or 'saliya' are used occasionally in some parts of Kuwait. The net can vary between 3 m and 6 m in diameter and usually has a mesh size of 32-40 mm. The hand rope, which is attached to the centre of the net by means of a brass ferule, is usually about 13 m in length. In order to cast the net the fisherman stands in the water with the net half slung over his shoulder. With a twisting motion of the body the net is thrown up into the air in an arc so that it opens out in a circle and drops on to the surface of the water. Lead weights around the net's circumference sink and trap any fish under the canopy of the net. The fisherman then carefully draws the net to the shore so that the catch does not escape. Although an expert may make it appear very easy considerable skill is required to cast the saliya correctly.

Handlining still occurs in Kuwait waters, but is not as common as in the past. Each line carries one or two hooks, and up to nine lines may be used from one boat. More efficient methods have largely replaced handlining although angling, whether from boats or the coastline, has recently become an important pastime in Kuwait.

A very curious and probably ancient method of catching fish is used in Sulaibikhat Bay. This bay is a very treacherous area due to its enormous expanse of very soft mud which is impossible to cross on foot. A few of the local fishermen there-fore use a small wooden board to spread their weight and hence reduce the likelihood of sinking into the mud without trace. The fisherman either kneels on the board and rows himself across the surface of the mud with his hands, or alternatively holds on to the board with his hands and uses his legs as the means of propulsion. Either method allows the fisherman to travel swiftly and safely across the mud at low tide. Usually the fisherman balances a woven basket on the front of the board, in which to collect the flat fish for which he is looking.

Until the establishment of the industrial shrimp

Saliya. A fisherman has just thrown his cast net and it has taken up its characteristic shape before dropping onto the surface of the water. Generally cast nets are used at dusk (ASDF)

A fisherman returns on his board to the safety of the shore after catching tongue soles at low tide on the mud flats of Sulaibikhat Bay (ASDF).

fishery in Kuwait in 1959, shrimp were traditionally caught using the taroof in shallow waters. Shrimp are sometimes still caught using these nets, but only incidentally for the main catch is usually zobaidy. With the start of the industrial fishery the dhow fishermen developed the 'goufa' or scoop net which was like a giant push net. The goufa was about 2.6 m in width with a mesh size of 35-40 mm and operated in pairs towed close to the sides of the boat. It appears that the last goufa was used in Kuwait in 1978 and it is highly unlikely that this particular method of fishing will be seen again as it was unique to Kuwait. The area formerly fished using this gear included shallow water less than 2 m in depth in Kuwait Bay and the vicinity of Failaka Island. The goufa has now been totally replaced by modern shrimp trawls with otter boards.

Goufa. Fishermen preparing a goufa for their next fishing trip. This gear was known only from Kuwait and was designed specifically for the local boats and bottom conditions. Before being superceded by modern shrimp trawls, the boats normally towed a pair of goufas, one close to each side of the vessel, with the vertical pole sticking out of the water (NPvZ)

Shrimp market. These fishermen have just returned from sea and have carried their catch of shrimps to the beach for immediate sale. Shrimps are sold by the measure of a basket, one of which is seen at the extreme left of the picture (DPP)

Fish spears or 'gumbaar' are rarely used in Kuwait these days, although the blacksmiths in the souk will still manufacture them upon request. Normally fish spears are used for catching large relatively slow-moving fish and flat fish in shallow waters. This form of fishing is carried out in strong moonlight or on dark nights with the aid of a lantern. Under similar conditions another unusual method of catching fish in Kuwait is the use of a fish sword or 'saif'. The fisherman stands patiently in the water until a fish is attracted to the light, whereupon he kills it with a downward blow from the sword.

Pearl diving has been the subject of a number of articles and books but will be referred to only briefly. The fishing grounds, known as 'hair' or 'hairah', extend from the southern part of Kuwait along the coast of Saudi Arabia as far as Bahrain

Fish Spear or 'gumbaar' and, on the right, a fish sword or 'saif' lying against a cast net hanging on the wall (ASDF)

Tidal flat mooring. Before the construction of harbours, most of the fishing boats were usually hauled up on the tidal flats. Very few of the smaller wooden boats survive, most of them having been replaced by fibreglass speed boats (DAC)

Opposite: A fisherman strikes with his fish sword, 'saif'. The lantern serves the double purpose of attracting the fish and permitting the fisherman to see his quarry. The catch is kept in the woven basket (ASDF)

Blacksmith forging the barbed tip of a fish spear *(gumbaar)* (ASDF)

and Qatar. Local divers departed for the fishing grounds on dhows or booms some of which were powered by oars as well as sail. The divers remained at the fishing grounds for several weeks at a time, and, in the case of more southern venues for the whole season.

Diving from their dhows the crews worked in pairs, one diving 'ghais' and the other 'seeb' waiting to haul the diver to the surface when signalled to do so. Each diver, equipped with a noseclip 'iftaam' and a basket 'dayeen' in which to collect the pearl oysters, used to descend to the seabed with the aid of rocks 'hijara', 'idi' or 'rawaasi' attached to the neck or ankles as weights. On reaching the bottom the diver released the weights and the attendant hauled them to the surface by a rope 'zaibel'. When the diver was ready to be brought to the surface, he would tug on a second rope 'aidi' in order to be pulled to the surface as quickly as possible by the seeb.

Traditional pearl diving in Kuwait has been super-ceded by divers operating from small boats using a hookah compressed air system. It is still possible to buy sacks of pearl oysters in the Oyster Market at the Friday Souk and, for an additional charge, have them opened using a 'miflaaga' or oyster knife.

The pearl merchants still use the brass sieves or 'taasa' for separating the various size categories of pearls, each of which has its own name. From the largest to the smallest these are 'dana', 'hasabi', 'ras', 'betten', 'thail', 'ruaiba'a' and 'sahteet'.

A lucky find; two beautiful pearls in one oyster. Note the curved oyster knife *(miflaaga)* in the man's right hand (ASDF)

Opposite: Opening the pearl oyster at the Pearl Oyster Market at the Friday souk. Bags of oysters can be bought at the market if one wishes to try one's luck (ASDF)

An exceptionally large pearl nestling within the oyster. Such pearls are called face pearls *(goumaash al-wajh)*. They can be shaken out after opening (ASDF)

A selection of pearls, the result of several days of opening oysters. Mishapen pearls are usually found within the viscera and are called belly pearls *(goumaash al-kirsh)* (ASDF)

Conservation

By
Charles Pilcher

The preceding chapters have provided many examples of the diverse ways in which the animals and plants of Kuwait have adapted to their surroundings. Some mention has also been made of the impact of man's activities on the environment and here it is intended to consider the local situation further. What has not been stressed so far is that there is a reciprocal relationship between the organism and its environment, so that just as the environment influences the organism, so does the organism influence the environment and thereby other organisms within the community. The interaction of all the factors, biological and physical, in the community constitutes an ecosystem and the study of the intricate interdependence of all the components in an ecosystem is termed ecology.

Desert tracks. Most noticeable in spring, vehicles cause untold damage to vegetation simply by being driven in the desert. Desert plants have such a precarious hold that the passage of vehicles, on as few as four separate occassions, result in a permanent loss of plant cover (IW)

Motorway. As the population of Kuwait continues to grow so too does the volume of traffic: over 120,000 vehicles are added to the roads annually. Motorways designed to handle such volume of traffic have been constructed to link the separate industrial and residential areas (FAM)

Many modern societies are characterised by a concern with increasing economic growth, greater productivity and expansion, all of which can be achieved only by further industrialisation and all that this entails. The adverse impact that the demand for more factories, more roads, more energy, more water, etc., has on the environment is realised by all too few. If prompted, many people in such societies would ask the question, "Why should we be bothered with ecology?". The answer is very simple: ultimately man's future depends on the way in which he treats the environment now, but it is not only a matter of ensuring that future generations will have material resources available. The management of the environment must also strive for the preservation of those qualities that will enable individuals to enjoy a rich and full life. Such qualities are difficult to define but they certainly include access to open unspoilt spaces, natural wild scenery and all forms of wildife to study and admire. Only by possessing a knowledge of the principles controlling the maintenance of ecosystems can man hope to treat the environment sympathetically and effectively. However, before elaborating on the need for a broad environmental approach to conservation in Kuwait it must be stressed that it would be totally unrealistic to argue that we must resist all change in attempts at conservation.

Conservation can be practised at any level and on any scale but, since recent surveys of remote parts of the earth have revealed signs of pollution by man-made chemicals carried there by winds and oceanic currents, it has become clear that environmental policies will have to be considered and implemented on an international, indeed world-wide, basis. This chapter will deal with issues on a less grand scale but which, from the point of view of Kuwait's natural heritage, are nonetheless vitally important.

A large proportion of the world's oil is produced in and around the Arabian Gulf and this small State of Kuwait is the third largest oil-producer in the Middle East. Much of the oil is transported by sea from coastal refineries and marine loading terminals. It is appropriate therefore to start by considering the marine environment, because the potential for an ecological disaster caused by pollution from spilled oil or effluents from related industries is so enormous that it has become a matter of concern for all countries bordering the Gulf. An attempt is therefore being made at an international level to co-operate in minimising the extent and likelihood of pollution. Kuwait has played an important role in this attempt and in 1980 representatives from all the countries concerned met here to formulate an outline of a project known as the Kuwait Action Plan, a scheme given the full support of the United Nations. The reasons for the potential for ecological disaster are manifold. Firstly, as the chapter on marine life has stressed, the waters of the Gulf are highly saline and conditions analogous to those of terrestrial deserts prevail. This means that there is little latitude in the tolerance of the ecosystems and it is not difficult to appreciate why the Gulf has been described as 'fragile' by ecologists. The severity of any oil spill will be exacerbated by the Gulf's oceanographic characteristics. The narrowness of the Straits of Hormuz restricts the circu-

Hydrogen sulphide stripper. The most productive conservation measures occur when environmental and industrial interests coincide. Environmentalists require the removal of hydrogen sulphide from crude oil because it pollutes the atmosphere, industrialists also require its removal because it is then possible to ship Eocene crude oil directly (MIK)

lation and exchange of waters and reduces mixing, dilution and oxygenation of the oil, factors that normally help to disperse it.

Inevitably marine oil spills have occurred in the Gulf, one of the most serious happening in the south as recently as late 1980, when an oil rig 'blew out'. Sadly this particular incident led to the serious pollution by heavy crude oil of at least half the coastline of Qatar at the southern end of the Gulf. What the consequences of this environmental disaster will be have yet to be established but experience from similar events elsewhere indicates that the inevitable effects on the fish, shrimps, crabs and other marine life, as well as on the rich population of seabirds there, will be tragic.

Refining plant. Since pollution control measures often involve some form of chemical separation or filtration of the pollutants it is much easier and less costly to incorporate them at the design stage of a refinery. The Government decided that atmospheric pollution from the high levels of sulphur in Kuwait's oil should be reduced and modern plants are built accordingly (MIK)

Shrimp catch. In the market place a fisherman displays the fruits of several hours of hard labour. Many such fishermen depend on the continued existence of commercially viable fishing grounds in and around Kuwait Bay. Excessive coastal development and other marine pollution will adversely affect the Bay's productivity and scenes like this one will become part of history (MIK)

Seabirds that have become contaminated are unable to fly and during attempts at preening their plumage may ingest the oil so that they usually die through starvation or poisoning. Once such an oil spill occurs, the high temperatures usually prevailing in the region cause the lighter petroleum fractions to evaporate so that the residue becomes heavy and tar-like. When this oil-tar residue settles on the beach it forms a thick, heavy blanket that literally suffocates organisms trapped below. Fortunately, surveys have shown that Kuwait's beaches are only slightly contaminated but the problem is that impacted tar may persist on Gulf beaches for more than six months.

Obviously accidents such as that mentioned above are disastrous for the marine environment, but there is an equally serious problem that is constantly with us; this is the problem of pollution resulting from deballasting, tank-washing and slop-disposal, all of which are routine activities in the operation of oil tankers.

Oil terminal. Over half of Kuwait's crude oil exports are loaded into tankers at Sea Island or the Single Point Mooring shown here. Despite being over 12 km offshore, the built-in safety precautions and constant maintenance make loading oil one of the safest aspects of its transport. Deballasting and shipping accidents are of far more importance in causing oil-slick pollution (KOC)

In addition to the destructive effects of oil pollution on the fragile marine ecosystems, there is a further serious aspect. A major oil spill could seriously foul the water produced by the seawater distillation plants for human needs and on which the country is vitally dependent. The Government of Kuwait has recognised the dangers of these activities and has taken steps to prevent them by enacting legislation to penalise those responsible for polluting the sea with oil or its residues.

Since the first exports of oil in 1946, Kuwait's economic growth has been dramatic, a phenomenon that has been reflected in the extremely rapid development of a variety of industrial activities. The country now has oil refineries, petrochemical and fertiliser plants, steel mills, brick and asbestos factories and numerous small industries. There are also power-generating stations and massive desalination plants. The main industrial complex is located at Shuaiba, about 50 km south of the city on a site that was carefully chosen to minimise the adverse effects of the various effluents on the country as a whole. This was possible because the prevailing winds are mainly northerly and north-westerly and generally, therefore, gaseous effluents are carried away from populated areas out over the sea or coastal desert. A secondary complex has been established in Shuwaikh on the perimeter of the western suburbs.

Shuwaikh industrial area. Once well removed from the residential areas Shuwaikh is now surrounded by them and the heavy industrial plants which cause atmospheric pollution are being relocated in another area. An unfortunate economic reality of commercial life is that such moves are costly and would not be made without Government legislation forcing the issue (FAM)

Shuwaikh Port. Any country which imports the majority of its raw materials, food and consumer goods needs extensive port facilities. In such cases environmental issues must be incidental and the sacrifice of sections of coastline is inevitable. Since port development in Kuwait is limited to Shuwaikh and Shuaiba the environmental degredation is minimised (FAM)

Desalination plant. Providing essential fresh water supplies to an arid region, the value of desalination plants is beyond doubt. In modern societies, however, the scale of operations is often so vast that what must be questioned is the long-term cost of marine pollution and whether or not alternative, less hazardous methods of purification are more economical (DAC)

Any country undergoing rapid industrialisation is faced with problems of controlling pollution by effluents detrimental to the environment and Kuwait, of course, is no exception. The Government has given these matters great consideration and ten years ago it established the Pollution Control Centre of the Shuaiba Area Authority to deal with them. Among the problems being dealt with by the Centre are: the fertiliser plants at Shuaiba discharge ammonia and hydrogen sulphide in their waste-water and the chlorine-producing plant in Shuwaikh loses mercury to the nearshore regions. In addition, many synthetic chemical compounds discharged by the petrochemical plants find their way into the Gulf and some are known to be harmful to marine life, even at very low concentrations. The Centre has met with a good deal of success and over the past few years has achieved a drastic reduction in pollution by ammonia and hydrogen sulphide. Moreover it has formulated a plan to make use of suitable land disposal of industrial waste-water instead of discharge into the sea.

One of the impressive achievements in Kuwait is the provision of fresh water and electrical power to meet evergrowing domestic, commercial and industrial needs. These services are obviously essential to the welfare and comfort of the whole population but the power and desalination plants

303

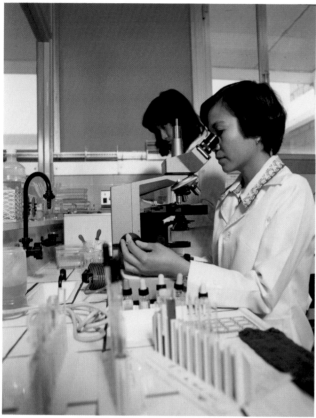

Pollution monitoring. Ranging from heavy metals to pollen, many health hazards only can be detected by careful laboratory analysis. Such detection procedures are often time consuming and costly to implement, but nevertheless are an essential part of any government's environmental protection policy (FAM)

Khiran. Captured several years ago, this tranquil scene no longer exists. Chalet owners, in their attempts to enjoy such scenes, have been instrumental in their disappearance (JNBB)

at Shuaiba, Shuwaikh and Dohah do present a further hazard to the marine environment through thermal pollution caused by the release of spent cooling water. In addition there is the adverse effect of emptying the highly concentrated brine back into the sea, an operation that may have unfortunate consequences for Kuwait Bay in the environs of Dohah. Because of the relatively poor circulation in the Bay and its already high salinities and temperature, the discharge of warm concentrated brine is likely to have a progressively deleterious effect on the marine flora and fauna. However, Government-sponsored research is seeking alternative ways of producing fresh water and utilising alternative energy sources, which will remove or minimise these adverse effects on the marine environment. At the present time work in government establishments is actively proceeding to develop a large scale process for desalinating sea-water by reverse osmosis, a process that will abolish thermal pollution. Moreover, the development of solar energy systems, which should have little adverse effect on the environment, will also reduce the problems of pollution caused by conventional power generating stations.

The countries bordering the Gulf have experienced an unprecedented growth in population and rate of urban development in recent years, and this is especially true of Kuwait. As a result, marine pollution by sewage effluents has become a serious problem because an unacceptably high quantity of insufficiently treated sewage enters the waters of the Gulf. A considerable amount of raw sewage from small coastal communities and illegal linkups with the recently rebuilt storm water drainage system finds its way into the sea. In small quantities the nutrients contained within the effluent are beneficial and in some locations, for example around Kuwait Bay, small beds of reeds flourish and provide shelter for migratory birds during their passage through the country. Above a critical level the sewage effluent becomes highly damaging to the existing ecosystem because excessive bacterial and algal growth consumes too much oxygen to the detriment of the other organisms. Moreover, there is the hazard of disease to the fishermen and bathers.

Reed-bed at sewage outflow. An outflow of waste-water containing sewage from a coastal community has permitted reed-beds to become established. These provide shelter and a seasonal abundance of insect life for migrating birds, but there is the risk of a health hazard from such inadequately treated effluent (CWTP)

The reed beds are an accidental and sometimes ephemeral product of sewage outflow but this waste effluent has been used deliberately and successfully to initiate tree plantations, which become self-supporting. Further afforestation is part of the agricultural diversification plan for the country and it is clear that the establishment of a naturally regenerating forest cover would be extremely beneficial. Some of the long-term effects of afforestation would be stabilisation of the soil, localised reductions in the severity of dust storms and a modification of the climate by reducing wind speed and providing shade. There would also be an undoubted recreational value since the established parks, gardens and wooded areas are already used to capacity.

Freshwater pool at Jahra. Man-made pools such as that shown here provide habitats for a variety of animals and plants and are potentially ideal wintering quarters for migrant waders, ducks and herons. This pool at Jahra was the largest area of standing fresh water to be found in Kuwait and could have provided an important part of a nature reserve (CWTP)

Rapid urbanisation has also led to the destruction of the natural beaches for long stretches of the shoreline from Sulaibikhat to Salmiyah. Huge amounts of demolition debris arising from housing development and other construction projects have been dumped along the shoreline together with vast quantities of unsightly rubbish. Among the adverse effects immediately apparent are the irreversible destruction of large areas of the mud-skipper breeding grounds in Sulaibikhat and the near annihilation of a unique colony of fiddler crabs *(Uca* spp.) near Shuwaikh port. Whilst it is true to say that some of this activity has been essential in the extension of the port facilities and the construction of the sea clubs, the extent of the infill will gradually impair the inshore environment

to the detriment of the existing marine flora and
fauna. The stretches of coastline referred to are
also host to the thousands of seabirds, waders,
herons and ducks that spend the winter months in
Kuwait and it is reasonable to assume that the
systematic destruction of their feeding-grounds can
only be detrimental to these species. Gradually
the new shoreline will become inhabited by members of a marine rocky shore community but the
ecological disruption is unlikely to be reversed for
large tracts of the coast.

As has happened elsewhere in the world,
industrialisation and urbanisation have resulted in
atmospheric pollution, which is particularly severe
in areas around the industrial zones. Most fossil
fuels have a high sulphur content and this is
certainly true of Kuwait's crude oil. Combustion
of the oil derivatives produced in the refineries
results in the formation of various oxides of
sulphur, including sulphur dioxide, and hydrogen
sulphide gas is given off from the evaporating pits,
where separation of oil and water is carried out.

The locality of the freshwater pool at Jahra. After draining of the Jahra
pool all that remains is an unsightly expanse of rubbish. Much of the
released water still lies in shallow puddles between the original location of
the pool and the coast, and the reason for destroying the pool is not
evident. This area was photographed during the winter shortly after being
drained, but the advent of the hot dry summer will see the death of the
reed-beds and the semi-aquatic vegetation (CWTP)

Atmospheric pollution. Noxious smelling gases and highly coloured effluents from industrial processes are the easiest pollutants to identify. Of far more importance and danger are the invisible, insiduously cumulative poisons that are also produced and which require careful, laboratory assisted monitoring programmes over long periods (DPP)

Demolition infill in Sulaibikhat Bay. Demolition debris and rubbish are being used to reclaim the extensive mudflats of Sulaibikhat Bay. In some cases irreparable damage to the intertidal marine communities will occur, even by the infilling of small areas, owing to the interdependence of the flora and fauna of the various zones (CWTP)

Apart from their foul odours, both hydrogen sulphide and sulphur dioxide are poisonous and the latter dissolves in water to produce an acidic solution that is generally destructive to living organisms. Industrial activities have also led to a high dust content of the air, which is not only a cause of physical discomfort but is also a hazard to human health.

Urbanisation and the apparent attractions of an affluent society have had other adverse effects on the environment of Kuwait. There has been a large movement of the indigenous Bedouin population from their native areas into the cities, resulting in the desert ecosystems, of which they were an important part, being disturbed. Many of these people still retain ties with their traditional rural

Housing development. Like much in Kuwait, urban development has proceeded at an astounding rate in the last few years and new housing areas are now found in what was previously open desert. Some of the housing accomodates bedouin who were originally nomadic members of Kuwait's society (DPP)

ways, which under modern conditions has brought about degradation of the desert environment. The possession of motor vehicles has made the Bedouin more mobile and they are now able to transport substantial quantities of water and fodder from urban stations to their livestock in the nearby

Extent of infill in west Shuwaikh. A view towards Shuwaikh port illustrates the extent of the infill which is to allow the building of new roads and recreational areas. The original shoreline can be seen curving away to the far right of the picture (CWTP)

Infill. An all too common scene around the Gulf, the infilling of the coastline provides valuable and immediately available land. The long-term consequences of this policy, however, is that as the Gulf's productive intertidal areas diminish so too will the catches of fish and shrimp (TCV)

A reflection of the changing desert scene. By transporting fodder and water to their flocks of sheep and goats the Bedouin are able to maintain a greater number of animals than the available grazing would normally support. As a result, great pressure is placed upon the desert vegetation and plant cover is fast disappearing from some areas (TCV)

desert. As a result, conditions are becoming more like those found in Sudan for example, where areas around water bore-holes have become deserts through over-grazing caused by too many animals being maintained beyond the carrying capacity of the environment. Similarly in Kuwait, natural vegetation cover is being destroyed causing potentially productive soil to be lost. Young shoots that appear are immediately devoured by the goats, sheep and to a lesser extent camels, so that plant growth and reproduction are often prevented and the soil becomes increasingly infertile. Moreover, woody shrubs that have managed to reach maturity are often cut down or even uprooted to provide kindling for fires, either by the Bedouin themselves or by campers. Without the protection of vegetation the shallow topsoil is being blown or washed away and further impoverished. It is difficult to know how this problem can be overcome, but resettlement of the Bedouin in small rural communities around their original localities and the application of range management techniques to prevent overgrazing of the desert are two approaches currently in operation.

Ecological effects of grazing. The marked contrast in the density and extent of plant cover inside and outside the fenced area illustrates the impact of overgrazing on desert vegetation. Soil laid bare in this way gradually becomes impoverished through lack of humus formation and the loss of wind-blown fertile topsoil (TCV)

Increasing affluence, continuing urbanisation and a steadily growing population are also causes of other pressures on the desert and even the marine environment. More people have leisure time and are able to afford a wide range of recreational pursuits. With the ever-increasing motor traffic in all parts of the desert, habitats for plants and small animals are being churned up, compacted or otherwise destroyed. Campers and day trippers leave their unsightly rubbish behind to add to that strewn about by the Bedouin. A somewhat similar story can be told about the state of the beaches and seabed both in nearshore areas and around the islands in the Gulf. Most of the discarded matter is not biodegradable and consequently rubbish is accumulating in some areas at an alarming rate. In view of the government's tremendous efforts to enhance the environment by keeping the streets, parks and gardens clear of litter and garbage and by planting trees and flowers in urban areas, it seems a great pity that the population at large has not developed an awareness of, and

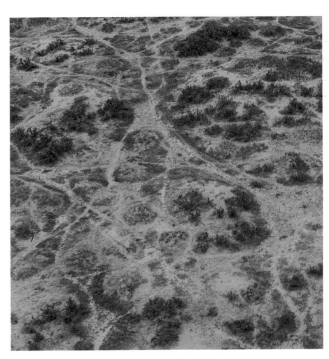

A network of tracks. When viewed from the air many regions of Kuwait's desert are seen to be criss-crossed by numerous vehicle tracks. Motor vehicles have largely replaced the traditional beasts of burden and are taken into every kind of locality by Bedouin, campers and day-trippers. Many habitats are lost as a result (DAC)

Afforestation. The establishment of a forested belt surrounding the greater urban area of Kuwait City is planned for the future. This section at Jahra is already well-established and provides a valued recreational area (GWW)

sympathy for, their environment. Ultimately this can only be achieved by a programme aimed at educating the public and fortunately the Environmental Protection Council, established by Ministerial Decree, has been active in attempting this, but much still needs to be done.

Along with boating and fishing, sub-aqua swimming has become a popular sport and both the coral reefs and the fish that they support are being seriously depleted by uncontrolled removal. On the commercial scale fishing has a long history in Kuwait and the demands of an ever-growing population have had a great impact on the fish resources of the Gulf. The Government has long recognised the potential dangers of over-fishing and it has encouraged and financed research and development programmes aimed at counteracting these dangers. Some of these programmes have been concerned with the ecology of the fish and shrimps that are important as food sources so that rational management policies may be determined.

Marine vandalism. All too often divers collect pieces of coral and other marine organisms as souvenirs of their visits to the seabed. For the corals this must be considered as verging on the criminal for not only do corals take many years to grow but those in Kuwait waters are also relatively rare (RW)

One such policy that has recently been implemented is that of a 'close season' in shrimp fishing. In order to allow the shrimps to breed and thus replenish stocks the Government has banned fishing from the beginning of February to the end of June each year. Yet other programmes have been devoted to breeding and rearing important varieties of fish with the intention of establishing fish farms on a commercially viable scale. In this way the natural population of endangered species of fish will have a significant degree of protection.

A further 'leisure sport' which is strictly illegal and which does a great deal of damage to wildlife, is that of shooting wild animals and birds. The government has banned the using of guns in Kuwait and although the police regularly check on localities known to be frequented by hunters, with their many other duties it is not possible for policemen to be on patrol all the time. As was pointed out in the Chapter on birds, Kuwait is on two migration routes and for this reason many species pass through the country during spring and

Pile of dead raptors. These birds, shot by hunters, were collected in a matter of minutes in the locality of the pool at Jahra. They were obviously killed for fun and were not intended to be eaten. Most of the corpses are Kestrels, which make easy targets as they hover whilst scanning the ground for prey (WAS)

autumn. Fresh water and cover can be found in only a few locations here so a large proportion of these migrants are attracted to a very small area; in their large numbers they are easy targets for people with guns. Some of the species migrating through Kuwait, especially the raptors, have been steadily on the decline in the Western Palaearctic Zone over the past two decades owing to the excessive use of agricultural chemicals in their breeding areas and the destruction of nesting sites. It is a tragedy that their numbers should be further reduced through unnecessary killing by hunters here. Already a number of species, of which the Houbara Bustard *(Chlamydotis undulata)* is a well known example, have become extinct in Kuwait. Uncontrolled hunting by individuals in motor vehicles armed with automatic shotguns also led to the extinction of the Dorcas Gazelle *(Gazella dorcas)*.

Across the globe man's activities have had a profound effect on the environment and its flora and fauna and from all that has been said here it is clear that this is also true for Kuwait. Industrial, urban and agricultural development, as well as an increasing demand for recreational facilities, has inevitably had, and will continue to have, an impact. If we are to show a responsible attitude to future generations and to our fellow living creatures, we must strive for ecological conservation and avoid needless and destructive change.

Urban development. Together with parks and gardens, the planting of trees and shrubs along the verges of the new motorways help to make the environment more attractive. The main function of motorway plantations, however, is to stabilize the soil and prevent its erosion during sand- and thunderstorms (FAM)

Bibliography

By
The Editors

COUNTRY & CLIMATE

Al Kulaib, A. M. *Weather and Climate of Kuwait.* Director General of Civil Aviation, Meteorological Section, Climatological Section, State of Kuwait. Undated, circa 1975.

Cloudsley - Thompson, J.L. *The Desert.* Orbis, London, 1977.

Cloudsley - Thompson, J.L. and **Chadwick, M.J.** *Life in Deserts.* Foulis, London, 1964.

Fuchs, W., Gattinger, T.G. and **Holzer, H.F.** (Eds.) *Explanatory Text to the Synoptic Geological Map of Kuwait.* The Geological Survey of Austria, Vienna, 1968.

Safar, M.I. *Meteorology and its Role in Economic and Social Development.* (in Arabic) Director General of Civil Aviation, Meteorological Section, Climatological Section, State of Kuwait. Undated, circa 1975.

VEGETATION

Alami, R., Macksad, A. and **El-Gindy, A.R.** *Medicinal Plants in Kuwait.* Al Assria Printing Press, Kuwait. Undated, circa 1960.

Dickson, V. *The Wild Flowers of Kuwait and Bahrain.* Allen and Unwin, London, 1955.

Mandaville, J. Jr. *The Wild Flowers of Northern Oman.* Illustrated by D. Bovey. Bartholemew Books, London, 1978.

Polunin, O. *Flowers of Europe.* Oxford University Press, Oxford, 1969.

Migahid, A.M. *Flora of Saudi Arabia.* 2 Volumes. Riyadh University Publication, Riyadh, 1978.

LAND INVERTEBRATES

Borror, D.J., Delong, D.M. and **Triplehorn, C.A.** *An Introduction to the Study of Insects.* 4th edition. Holt, Rinehart and Winston, New York, 1976.

Brown, G.W. (Ed.). *Desert Biology.* 2 volumes. Academic Press, New York, 1968, 1974.

Cloudsley - Thompson, J.L. *Spiders, Scorpions, Centipedes and Mites.* Pergamon Press, Oxford, 1968.

LAND INVERTEBRATES, continued

Goodden R. *British Butterflies, A Field Guide.* David and Charles, London, 1978.

Lyneborg, L. *Moths in Colour.* Illustrated by N. Jonsson and translated by K. Campbell-Ferguson. Blandford Press, Poole, Dorset, 1976.

Wittmer, W. and **Buttiker, W.** (Eds.). *Fauna of Saudi Arabia.* 2 Volumes. Pro Entomologica Natural History Museum, Augustinergasse 2 CM-4001 Basel, 1979, 1980.

Zahradnik, J. *A Field Guide in Colour to Insects.* Illustrated by F. Severa. Octopus Books, London, 1977.

REPTILES

Anderson, S.C. *The Turtles, Lizards and Amphisbaenians of Iran.* University Microfilms International, Ann Arbor, Michigan, 1976.

d'A Bellairs, A. *Reptiles.* Hutchinson University Library, London, 1968.

Gallagher, M.D. *The Amphibians and Reptiles of Bahrain.* Private Printing, Bahrain, 1971.

Heatwole, H. *Reptile Ecology.* University of Queensland Press, St. Lucia, 1976.

BIRDS

Bruun, B. and **Singer, A.** *The Hamlyn Guide to Birds of Britain and Europe.* Hamlyn, London, 1970.

Gallagher, M.D. *Birds of Oman.* Illustrated by M. Woodcock. Quartet Books, London, 1980.

Heinzel, H., Fitter, R.S.R. and **Parslow, J.L.F.** *The Birds of Britain and Europe with North Africa and The Middle East.* Collins, London, 1972.

Porter, R.F., Willis, I., Christensen, S. and **Nielsen, B.P.** *Flight Identification of European Raptors.* 2nd. Edition. T. and A.D. Poyser Ltd., Berkhamstead, 1976.

MAMMALS

Harrison, D.L. *Mammals of the Arabian Gulf.* Allen & Unwin, London, 1981.

Harrison, D.L. *Mammals of Arabia.* 3 Volumes. Benn, London, 1964, 1968, 1972.

Schmidt - Nielsen, K. *Desert Animals: Physiological Problems of Heat and Water.* Oxford University Press, London, 1964.

MARINE LIFE

Basson, P.W. Burchard, J.E., Hardy, J.T. and **Price, A.R.G.** *Biotopes of the Western Arabian Gulf.* Arabian American Oil Company, Dhahran, 1977.

Carcasson, R.H. *A Field Guide to the Coral Reef Fishes of the Indian and West Pacific Oceans.* Collins, London, 1977.

George, D. and **George, J.** *Marine Life: An Illustrated Encyclopedia of Invertebrates in the Sea.* Harrap, London, 1979.

Jessen, K. and **Sparch R.** *Danish Scientific Investigations in Iran.* Volumes 1-4. Einer Munksgaard, Copenhagen 1939-49.

Kuronuma, K. and **Abe, Y.** *Fishes of Kuwait.* Kuwait Institute for Scientific Research, State of Kuwait, 1972.

Relyea, K. *Inshore Fishes of the Arabian Gulf.* Allen and Unwin, London, 1981.

SEASHELLS

Dance, S.P. *The Encyclopedia of Shells.* Blandford Press, London, 1974.

Lindner, G. *Seashells of The World.* Blandford Press, London, 1978.

Morton, J.E. *Molluscs.* 4th Edition. Hutchinson University Press, London, 1967.

Smythe, K. *Seashells of the Arabian Gulf.* Allen & Unwin, London, 1982.

TRADITIONAL FISHING

Al-Kholy, A., and **Solovjov, B.S.** (Eds.) *Kuwait Fisheries.* (In Arabic) Ministry of Public Works. Kuwait. Undated, circa 1975.

Hawkins, C.W. *The Dhow: An Illustrated History of the Dhow and Its World.* Nautical Historical Record Series, Lymington, Nautical Publishing Company Ltd., Hants., 1977.

Villiers, A.J. *The Sons of Sinbad.* Hodder and Stoughton, London, 1940.

CONSERVATION

Allen, R. *How to Save the World : Strategy for World Conservation.* Kogan Page, London, 1980.

Al-Shayji, N. *Science and Technology and the Environment.* Kuwait National Symposium on Science and Technology for Development, Kuwait Institute for Scientific Research, May 1978.

Brainerd, J.W. *Nature Study for Conservation.* Macmillan Company, New York, 1971.

GENERAL READING

Cloudsley - Thompson, J.L. *Desert Life.* Pergamon Press, Oxford, 1965.

Buxton, P.A. Animal Life in Deserts. Arnold, London, 1955.

Hadley, N.F. *Environmental Physiology of Desert Organisms.* Halsted Press, New York, 1975.

Hills, E.S. (Ed.) *Arid Lands.* Methuen, London, 1966.

Jaeger, E.C. *Desert Wildlife.* Stanford University Press. Stanford, 1961.

Pond, A.W. *The Desert World.* Nelson, New York, 1962.

Tate, R. *Desert Animals.* Harper and Row, New York, 1971.

McGinnies, W.M. (Ed.) *Deserts of the World.* University of Arizona Press, Tuscon, 1968.

Wagner, F.H. *Wildlife of the Desert.* Harry N. Abrams/Chanticleer Press, New York, 1980.

Seashell sizes

By Charles Johnson

Shell sizes can be important in species identification and the reproduction of the seashell plates here at specific magnifications is designed to facilitate such identification.

**Rock and Coral-
dwelling Bivalves.**

Magnification $\times \frac{1}{2}$.

1. Scallop
   (*Chlamys ruschenbergerii*)

2. Pearl oyster
   (*Pinctada margaritifera*)

3. Wing oyster
   (*Pteria marmorata*)

4. Thorny oyster
   (*Spondylus gaederopus*)

5. Jewel-box shell
   (*Chama pacifica*)

6. Arc shell
   (*Anadara ehrenburgi*)

Chestnut olive shell
(*Ancilla castenea*).
Magnification $\times$ 1.

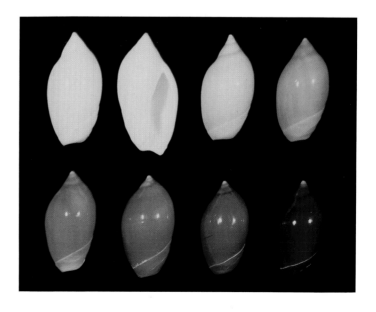

Rock-dwelling Gastropods.

Magnification × ½.

1. Graceful Cowry
   (*Cypraea gracilis*)

2. Freckled Cowry
   (*Cypraea lentiginosa*)

3. Onyx Cowry
   (*Cypraea onyx succincta*)

4. Thrush Cowry
   (*Cypraea turdus*)

5. Murex
   (*Hexaplex kuesterianus*)

6. Variable Thais
   (*Thais mutabilis*)

7. *Rapana bulbosa*

Sand and Mud-dwelling Bivalves.

Magnification × ½.

1. Pen shell
   (*Pinna muricata*)

2. Window-pane Oyster
   (*Placuna placenta*)

3. Razor shell
   (*Solen* sp.)

4. Fluted Little Heart Shell
   (*Cardita ffinchi*)

5. Sunset shell
   (*Gari occidens*)

Arabian Venus Clam
(Circenita callipyga, f. *arabica)*
Magnification × $\frac{3}{4}$.

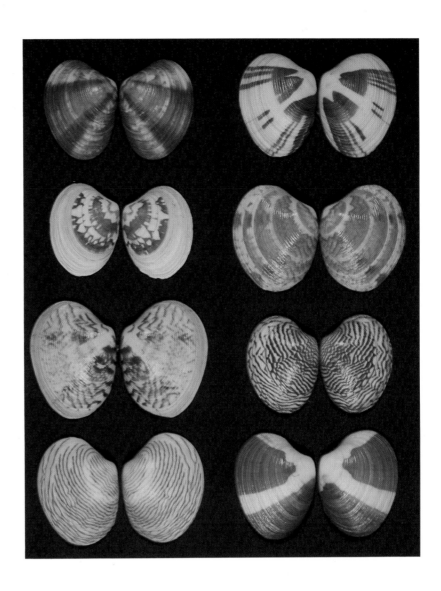

**Clusterwink, nutmegs
and other Gastropods.**

Magnification × 1.

1. Banded Nutmeg
    (Cancellaria sp.*)*

2. Staircase Nutmeg
    (Trigonostoma scalariformis)

3. Three-ribbed Capshell
    (Amathina tricostata)

4. Ribbed clusterwink
    (Planaxis sulcatus)

5. Slipper limpet
    (Crepidula walshi)

6. Pheasant shell
    (Phasianella solida)

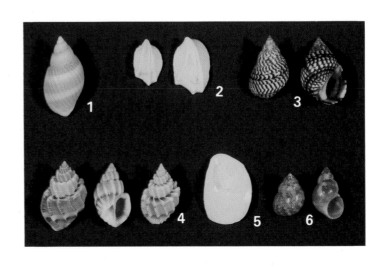

Sand-dwelling Bivalves.

Magnification × $\frac{3}{4}$.

1. Ridged Sunset Shell
   (Asaphis violescens)
2. Painted Little Heart Shell
   (Cardita bicolor)
3. Lilac Trough Shell
   (Mactra lilacea)

4. Rough Cockle
   (Trachycardium lacunosum)
5. Brown Dog Cockle
   (Glycymeris lividus)
6. Ribbed Dog Cockle
   (Glycymeris maskatensis)

Frog shell

(Bursa spinosa).

Magnification × $\frac{3}{4}$.

Tusk Shells and Sand-dwelling Gastropods.

Magnification $\times \frac{3}{4}$.

1. Tusk shells
   (*Dentalium* sp.,
   Dentalium octangulatum)

2. Button topshell
   (*Umbonium vestiarium*)

3. Dogwhelk
   (*Nassarius arcularius plicatus*)

4. Speckled Moonshell
   (*Natica pulicaris*)

5. Carrier shell
   (*Xenophora corrugata*)

6. Banded Mitre Shell
   (*Vexillum osiridis*
       = *Pusia osiridis*)

7. Spindle shell
   (*Fusinus townsendi*)

8. Dove shell
   (*Mitrella blanda*)

9. Auger shell
   (*Terebra* sp.)

Other typical Kuwait Gastropods.

Magnification $\times \frac{3}{4}$.

1. Pearly baby's ear
   (*Stomatella sulcifera*)

2. Variegated Thais
   (*Thais savignyi*)

3. False Ormer
   (*Stomatia phymotis*)

4. Speckled Mitre
   (*Mitra bovei*)

5. Rock cerith
   (*Cerithium caeruleum*)

6. Screw shell
   (*Turritella ?auricincta*)

7. Turrid shell
   (*Inquisitor griffithi*)

331

Fishbone murex

Magnification × 1.

(Murex scolopax).

The smaller specimen is an average size adult, whereas the exceptionally large one measures 144 mm.

Limpets, topshells and others.

Magnification × 1.

1. False limpet
   (Siphonaria rosea)

2. Keyhole limpet
   (Diodora funiculata)

3. Turban shell
   (Turbo coronatus)

4. Banded Horn Shell
   (Cerithidea cingulata)

5. Strawberry topshell
   (Clanculus pharaonius)

6. Streaked topshell
   (Trochus erythraeus).

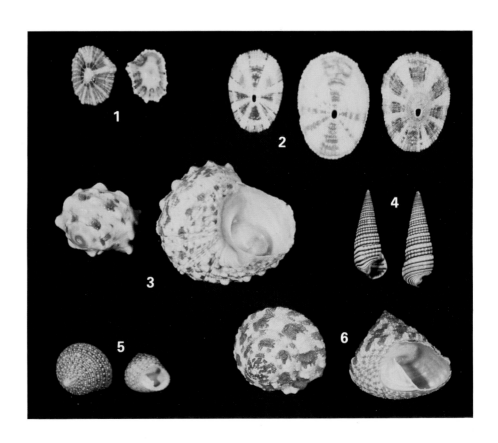

Sand-dwelling Gastropods.

Magnification × $\frac{1}{2}$.

1. Persian conch
   (Strombus decorus persicus)

2. Torpedo conch
   (Terebellum terebellum)

3. Arabian Tibia
   (Tibia insulaechorab curta)

4. Fishbone murex
   (Murex scolopax)

5. Bonnet shell
   (Phalium faurotis),

6. Bubble shell
   (Bulla ampulla)

Moonshells and other Gastropods.

Magnification × 1.

1. Tinted Moonshell
   (Polinices powisiana)

2. Paper Moonshell
   (Eunaticina papilla)

3. Lined Moonshell
   (Natica lineata)

4. False Moonshell
   (Vanikoro sulcata)

5. Wormshell
   (Serpulorbis sulcatus)

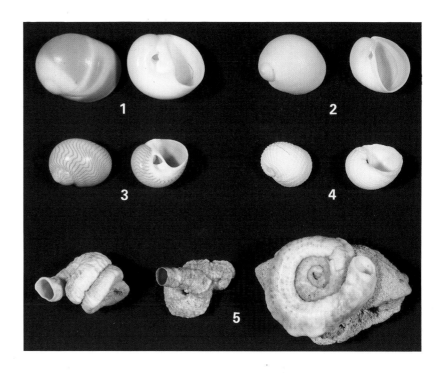

Scientific Names

Numerals in **'bold'** indicate a photograph of the
subject mentioned. Textual references may also
occur on the same page but are otherwise indicated
in 'roman'.

English Names

Numerals in **'bold'** indicate a photograph of the subject mentioned. Textual references may also occur on the same page but are otherwise indicated in 'roman'.

Designed, & Printed by Fahad Al Marzouk, Kuwait.

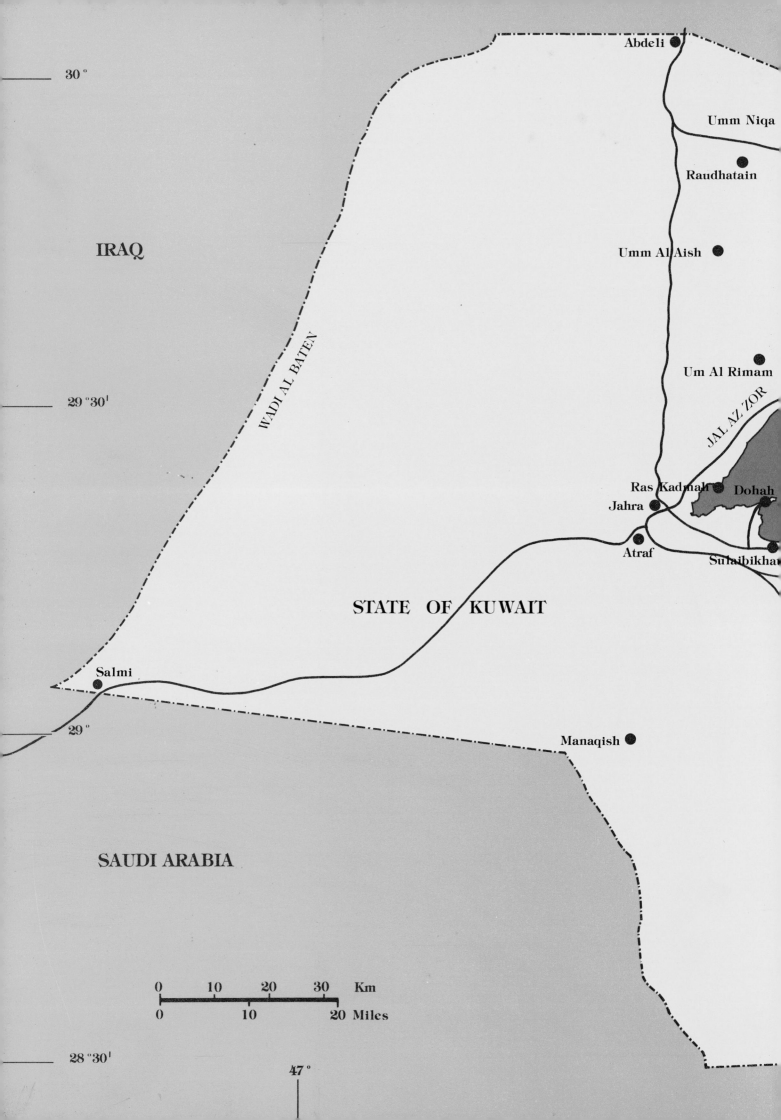

30°

IRAQ

29°30'

WADI AL BATEN

STATE OF KUWAIT

29°

Salmi

SAUDI ARABIA

28°30'

47°

Abdeli

Umm Niqa

Raudhatain

Umm Al Aish

Um Al Rimam

JAL AZ ZOR

Ras Kadmah   Dohah

Jahra

Atraf

Sulaibikhat

Manaqish

| 0 | 10 | 20 | 30 | Km |
| 0 | | 10 | | 20 Miles |